THE EMPIRE BUILDERS

BOOKS BY

Robert Ormond Case

VERNONIA PUBLIC LIBRARY

RULES

1. Four adult and two children's books may be taken out at one time.
2. Books may be kept for two weeks, and renewed for two weeks longer.
3. A fine of one cent per day is charged for every book kept longer than the time allowed.
4. Books lost must be paid for. For injury to books a fine is charged. See pamphlet for copy of laws.

Oregon Laws Relating to Public Libraries

Section 17. PENALTY FOR DEFACING BOOKS. Whoever wilfully or maliciously writes upon, injures, defaces, tears or destroys a book, plate, picture, engraving, map, newspaper, magazine, pamphlet, manuscript or statue belonging to a law, city, county, school district, state or other public or incorporated library, shall be punished by a fine of not less than $5.00 nor more than $50.00, or by imprisonment not exceeding six months.

Section 18. PENALTY FOR DETENTION OF BOOKS. Whoever wilfully or maliciously detains any book, newspaper, magazine, pamphlet or manuscript belonging to a law, city, county, school district, state or other public or incorporated library for thirty days after notice in writing from the librarian of such library, given after the expiration of time which by regulations of such library, such book, newspaper, magazine, pamphlet, or manuscript may be kept, shall be punished by a fine of not less than $5.00 nor more than $25.00, or by imprisonment not exceeding six months; provided, that the notice required by this section shall bear upon its face a copy of this section.

Yakima River

Snake River

River

Umatilla River

The Dalles

John Day River

Blue Mountains

OREGON

L. BAKER

THE
EMPIRE BUILDERS

BY

Robert Ormond Case

DOUBLEDAY & COMPANY, INC.

Garden City, New York

1947

DEDICATION

To my wife, Evelyn

AUTHOR'S PREFACE AND ACKNOWLEDGMENTS

MANY students of history are aware of the tremendous drama enacted on the giant stage known a century ago as the "Oregon Country"; a region extending roughly from the Rockies to the Pacific and from California to Alaska, comprising an area of some 470,000 square miles.

This was the final battleground, bloodless but decisive, in the age-old clash of expanding empires. The major scenes enacted in that giant amphitheater are familiar: the withdrawal of Spain and Russia from the North Pacific; the conflicting claims of Britain and the United States; the early despotism of the Hudson's Bay Company; and finally—the decisive factor which guaranteed this nation's title to the richest remaining segment of "free land" on the globe's surface—the covered wagon immigration westward from the Missouri.

Yet these were merely the mass effects, colorful but composite. Somewhere in that historic revue were key events and men: the incidents upon which the larger sweep of the drama depended; the men who stepped forth from the wings at the perfectly timed moment to speak their lines as indicated in the unchanging script.

To present these incidents in simple, dramatic form, and to recapture—insofar as the dimming record permits—something of the personality and character of the empire builders themselves, was the aim of this book.

Research for the book progressed in three stages. First general and specific historical texts were read to gain an over-all view of the enormous panorama. These texts included

Bancroft, Carey, Scott, Lyman, Parrish, Montgomery, and even Gaston's "History," which was read closely, not for its factual content but largely for the personal reminiscences the writer had obtained from pioneers still living when his manuscript was being assembled.

Next, having selected the historic incident deemed sufficiently significant to comprise one.of the 25 links in our chain, the outstanding personality connected with the incident was selected, and that individual was made to carry the major role in that particular drama.

Lastly, having selected the drama, the cast, and the setting, original sources were again consulted to gain every available clue to personality and facet of character, as well as to the proper sequence of events which would make the finished drama as historically accurate as possible. It was not often necessary to improvise scenes and sequences upon which the historic record was blank, but when it was necessary to do so the players were kept "in character" and spoke lines which logically would have been required by the known record.

Thus some fifty-odd books were read and analyzed, plus an enormous number of original diaries, letters, and reminiscences recorded in the Oregon Historical Society's files and quarterlies. In a few instances—unfortunately all too few after the passing of a century—descendants of the pioneers themselves added human touches, not elsewhere recorded, which had come down by word of mouth through succeeding generations.

These stories were first presented as a radio program over station KION in Portland, Oregon.* In book form they retain the original dialogue almost intact so that the series could readily be adapted to classroom presentation.

ROBERT ORMOND CASE

*Note. The program was the winner of a special Peabody Award as the outstanding radio program of its type during 1944.

CONTENTS

CONTENTS

THE EMPIRE BUILDERS

BEFORE 1790

Shortly after the Revolutionary War, trappers and traders from the Missouri brought back legends of a mighty river which was said to spring from the roots of the Rocky Mountains and thence flow westward to a forested and beautiful region bordering the Pacific.

Shoshone warriors had a name for the evergreen land through which the River of the West flowed: Oyer-un-gun, or "place of plenty." To Spanish adventurers it was Agua Aura, "gently falling water." Canadian fur traders preferred the Algonquin Wau-re-gan, or "beautiful water."

From one of these—or all of them—came the strange and haunting name: Oregon. Soon the entire region west of the Rockies was called the "Oregon Country."

It was the race to discover the River of the West, as the initial step in claiming title to the vast Oregon Country, that ushered in the first act of history's most colorful empire drama. The curtain rose almost simultaneously in three brilliant capitals of Europe: London, Madrid, and St. Petersburg —and on the provincial, night-shrouded docks of Boston Harbor.

I

DISCOVERY OF THE COLUMBIA

HIGH clouds hid the moon and stars that autumn night in Boston in the year 1790. Grogshops were ablaze on the hill, but down at the water front the great warehouses were black and silent. Many sailing ships were hidden in the outer darkness, the unseen water whispering against their barnacled hulls.

The sound was familiar and comforting to the man who stood on the shadowed pier, his teeth gripping an unlighted pipe. His was a well-known figure in Boston by day, buttoned to the neck in a sea jacket, smiling out of Yankee blue eyes; a friendly, rough-hewn man, browned by sun and storm but stamped with the look of command.

He was Captain Robert Gray, master of the small but sturdy ship *Columbia*.

Gray's fame as a daring shipmaster rested on a voyage concluded the previous year, when he had rounded the Horn and pushed boldly into the North Pacific. From there he had sailed the *Columbia* to China with a cargo of furs, traded for tea, and returned by way of the Cape of Good Hope—the first time the American flag had circled the globe.

There had been much glory in the exploit but little profit for the owners of the *Columbia*. Now, in an upstairs office above the pier, the owners were debating a second venture. They were seasoned gamblers, these Boston merchants. Seventeen years before they had gambled heavily on a shipment of tea. History called it the Boston Tea Party.

But tonight there were some timid souls among them. Gray could hear the voices of both the doubtful and bold rising up in hot argument.

"Gentlemen, we can't risk more capital on such a will-o'-the-wisp! What do we know about this River of the West? The Indians say it empties into the North Pacific, but who's seen it? Have the British? Have the Spanish? Who *knows?*"

"It's too far away! The Mississippi's near by. That's our field."

"But, my dear sir, the Mississippi belongs to Spain! The British are north of us. We're hemmed in! I say if there's a River of the West out there let's be the first to explore it. It's new country. Our destiny lies in the West!"

" 'Destiny,' Mr. Hatch? *I* was speaking of cash——"

Captain Gray could only wait, as he had waited for two hours past. His future was being decided up there. Also, though neither he nor the Boston merchants were aware of it, the pattern of enormous future events was being determined in these moments.

Finally it came to the vote.

"Let's have done with it, sirs! Who's for sending Captain Gray around the Horn to the Oregon Country?"

"Aye! . . . Aye!"

"Who votes no?"

"Gentlemen, I—I am wondering——"

"The ayes have it!" There was a brief burst of applause. "Mr. Hatch, will you please step to the window and call Captain Gray? I think he'll be pleased to hear our decision."

Captain Gray already knew. Boston men would never applaud a cautious vote! He drew erect in the darkness and stood on feet firmly planted: a big man and broad, hands thrust deep in his pockets, his teeth gripped exultantly on his pipe. He knew nothing, cared nothing, about the game of empire. The fairest adventure a fur trader could ask lay ahead. Outward bound! Headed for the Horn! . . .

4

The *Columbia,* fitted for a two-year cruise, faded from view of Boston Harbor on September 28, 1790. The next spring, in far-off London, an undersecretary from the Ministry rose up to address the Admiralty Board. There was no doubt or hesitancy here. Business more important than furs was on the agenda.

"My lords, you have heard the report of the Hudson's Bay Company. It brings the Nootka Sound matter to a head. If there *is* a great River of the West in that area we must find it at once and claim it for the Crown. Better still, let us claim the entire Pacific Coast from Monterey north. That will dispose of the matter."

"But I say—won't the Russians object? And the Spanish too?"

"Perhaps." The undersecretary could afford a touch of discreet amusement. Since the destruction of the Spanish Armada two centuries before, his Majesty's Minister and the lords of the Admiralty had seen eye to eye on global strategy. "But Sir Francis Drake was in those waters with the *Golden Hind.** Cook was there in 1778, searching for the Northwest Passage. That's quite enough, I think. 'Right of discovery,' you know . . . But we must act at once. I recommend for your approval placing Lieutenant George Vancouver in command of two ships and sending him immediately to the North Pacific."

The legend of the River of the West had also reached St. Petersburg. There, in the summer of 1791, the harsh voice of a courtier reflected the impatient ambition of the Czar:

"What is this, Baranov—you have come to ask *permission* to explore south from Nootka Sound? Who was first in the

---

*A chronicler aboard the *Golden Hind* during Drake's famous voyage in 1578 records that Drake touched somewhere on the Oregon coast, but a "stinkeing fogge" prevented fixing the exact latitude.

North Pacific? Vitus Bering, of Russia! Certainly you will explore south. Hurry back there, man! Lose no time. . . ."

And in the languid court of Spain:

"Señor Quadra—you will return to Monterey at once. You will proceed north to Nootka Sound. Our embassy at London tells us that the British are preparing to search for the River of the West. So—you will negotiate with the Russians, claiming all of the North Pacific. . . . You understand, Señor Quadra, it will be greatly to our advantage if you can establish our claims with the Russians *before* the British come. . . ."

Juan Francisco de la Bogeda y Quadra, commander of Monterey, sailed north to Nootka Sound in the spring of 1792. Lashed to his ship's deck were many barrels of good Barbados rum. He found a few Russian traders there but no person of importance.

This was a relief to the affable Quadra. One merely did one's best in these affairs of state. There was plenty of time. The Russians would not be the deciding factor, in any event; it would be those difficult British. The British, fortunately, were far away.

So they all went up to an old log hut on the hill. Quadra called it a "fort" and ran up the Spanish flag. The Russian traders smiled—and drank the rum. Baranov hadn't yet arrived with his instructions from the Czar. Who cared? Why worry about the fur trade or talk about empire when good fellows get together? So they drank day and night as summer strengthened, and sang and rolled empty barrels down the hill.

Vancouver's two ships were near by, however. They were creeping up the coast with the formidable sloop of war *Discovery* in the lead. Captain Vancouver and his lieutenant, Broughton, were on the bridge of the *Discovery*, studying

the strange, timbered shore line. Both Vancouver and Broughton carried themselves correctly, as befitted Royal Navy
men. In their view these were already British waters.

Near North Latitude 46° they came opposite a break in
the misty shore line and veered in as close as they dared.
Between a prominent headland and a low sandspit was a
long line of tossing foam. They could hear the sullen booming of surf. Could this be the mouth of the great River of
the West?

Vancouver spoke positively. "I think not, Broughton—it's
just another bay. We'll hurry on north."

Farther north they sighted a strange ship close inshore.
A little ship. There was something daring and confident and
gay in the way she footed along just outside the line of
surf. Skilled and daring seamen were aboard. No Russian
ship—and certainly no Spaniard—would venture that close
to the breakers.

"Get your glass on her, Broughton! What flag is she
flying?"

"I have it, sir. . . . My word—the American flag! The
Columbia of Boston."

Vancouver frowned. "Americans, eh? Run up a signal.
We'll hail them and find out what the blighters are up
to."

Gray answered the signal and came alongside. Vancouver
looked down at the *Columbia,* secretly amused. She was
sadly in need of paint. Captain Gray wore no uniform. He
was just a big, genial seafaring man with a habit of standing
erect, his hands thrust into the pockets of his sea jacket,
his teeth gripping an unlighted pipe. He seemed unimpressed
by the cannon on the forward deck. His manner was that of
a country person eager to gossip with a neighbor over a
garden hedge.

"Whither bound, Captain?" Vancouver inquired politely.
"You're doing a bit of exploring, perhaps?"

"Oh no—just looking for furs. I've been here since last summer. Say, did you notice the current coming out of that bay down below? I laid off there nine days a while back but couldn't get in. I'm on my way for another look. It might be that big River of the West!"

"Perhaps. One never knows. . . . We're bound for Nootka, Captain Gray. Shall we see you there?"

"Sure, sure—we'll have a regular visit. Nice country hereabouts, eh? Notice those big trees alongshore? I'll swear, if I was to tell the folks back in Boston——"

Vancouver soon brushed him off and sailed on north. He watched the *Columbia* dip over the southern horizon. There was a cold twinkle in his eye.

"Let him waste his time on that bay, Broughton. . . . An odd lot, these Yankees. A bit on the uncouth side, what?"

"But he'll bear watching, sir."

"Bah! He'll find no river."

On his way north Vancouver sighted and named Mount Rainier and Mount Baker. He explored and named Vancouver Island, Puget Sound, and other points. In late summer he put in at Nootka Sound.

Quadra received him in courtly fashion. Vancouver drank with him—discreetly—while the Russians grinned in the background. No formal business could be conducted until the social amenities were concluded. Actually, as both knew, there was little business to discuss. Spain's maritime power had crumbled steadily since the Armada. An impressive argument supporting "rights of discovery" were two British ships anchored within view of the fort, armed with cannon.

Then the Yankee ship *Columbia* tacked casually into the Sound. The Russians laughed. Quadra laughed. Beside the sloop of war *Discovery*, the *Columbia* was a tiny ship. No doubt Captain Gray was still looking for his big river. . . .

But Broughton dashed hurriedly up the hill and whispered in Vancouver's ear. Vancouver paled.

"Impossible, Broughton! The man's mad!"

"I doubt it, sir. He has charts. He took soundings."

"Have him and his charts aboard the *Discovery* at once."

Gray came aboard, pleased as a boy. He had discovered the great River of the West! It was one of the large rivers of the continent. Its mouth was the "bay" that Vancouver had passed by.

"We saw that bay, Captain Gray! So did Meares. That's no discovery."

"But did you or Meares cross the bar?" Gray demanded. "Did *you?*"

"Sure did. Look."

Gray spread the charts on the table. He had not only mapped the bay and the mouth of the great river; he had gone upstream and filled his casks with water. *Fresh water* . . . This was no idle claim; it *was* discovery.

"And I went ashore and claimed her for the United States. I don't take much stock in that gibberish, but you folks set store by it. So I did it fit and proper—waved a rusty cutlass in the air and all the rest of it. Even those naked heathen thought that was funny. . . . But the river's the thing— and she's ours! Yes, and all the land it drains. I've named it after my ship. She's a little ship and it's a big river, but I figure it's a good name—the Columbia!"

Vancouver studied the charts, his face grim and set. Here was a new grain of sand tossed into enormous and delicately balanced scales. It outranked this diplomatic mummery with Quadra. It placed title to the vast interior of the continent in jeopardy. Gray did not officially represent his country, true. He was little more than a vagabond trader. Yet, using Britain's own empire formula—"right of discovery"—he was claiming the river *and all the land it drained.* . . .

Gray was still talking in his bluff, friendly way.

"Take a look at the river on the way south. Take the

9

charts and copy them tonight. I'll pick them up in the morning."

Vancouver gave him a guarded, intent look. Could anybody be *that* naïve?

"Do you mean it, sir?"

"Why not? There's no hard feelings now that it's over and done. Sure, copy them. You'll need those soundings if you go inside."

"I will, indeed. . . . Where do you sail from here, Captain Gray?"

"Oh, up north again. One more landfall or two up there before I steer for the Horn."

It was perfect. Vancouver took the charts, copied them, then hurried south to the Columbia. He sent Broughton with the *Chatham* on a tour of exploration up the great river while he sailed on to Monterey with the *Discovery*. Broughton joined him there and they hastened around the Horn. They were in London long before Gray made it back to Boston.

Thus, easily the way was smoothed for the next move in the game which knew no rules. In due time a spokesman for the Ministry again addressed the Admiralty Board.

"Captain Vancouver has discovered the great River of the West, my lords. It appears to be a magnificent river, a great fur country. Lieutenant Broughton explored more than one hundred miles upstream, through incredible forests. He came to a mountain range and named two of the lofty peaks: Mount Hood and Mount St. Helens. Here are the charts of the river. . . . Er—there was a Yankee ship, commanded by a Captain Robert Gray of Boston, which entered the bay. By his own admission Gray was interested only in furs. . . . I have a suggestion to make, my lords. I recommend that we claim not only the river itself but all the land it drains. . . ."

The dignified old sea lords applauded. It was a good

report, a good summer's business for the Empire. "Bravo! Three cheers for Captain Vancouver!"

Captain Gray quitted the historic stage after he returned to Boston. He had not asked for glory. He was a shipmaster and trader; no more. His part played, he strode genially from the footlights into the shadowed wings. Even the time and manner of his death are unknown.

His exploit lived on. No subterfuge of global diplomacy could evade or ignore it. In the ensuing half century of controversy, his nation's strongest claim to the Oregon Country was established in that moment when Captain Robert Gray of Boston, without benefit of chart or pilot, laid his course unhesitatingly across the Columbia's thundering bar.

1792 – 1803

During the ten years following Gray's discovery of the Columbia River, Europe was at war. The three great powers claiming the Oregon Country—England, Spain, and Russia— were fighting for survival. Napoleon Bonaparte was master of all western Europe except England.

Yet the march of empire never halts. Out in North America the two British fur-trading companies—the Hudson's Bay and Northwest Company—were pushing westward. Yankee traders were exploring the Mississippi Valley, which was included in the enormous but vaguely defined territory of Louisiana. Title to Louisiana had again shifted to France, which dominated the entire Mississippi basin through its control of New Orleans.

Nevertheless, though the bulk of the continent inter- vened, the young but robust United States kept its ambitious eyes turned toward the Pacific. A great President's foresight extended the nation's borders to the Rockies in a single coup. A private citizen—an immigrant turned capitalist in the American way—made one of history's boldest singlehanded bids for the empire that lay beyond the Great Divide.

II

ASTOR'S FORT

IN AN office in Washington in 1803, a group of Cabinet members faced a large map of North America which hung on the wall. Beside it stood a plainly dressed man, studious of feature but emanating a quiet dignity and force. He was Thomas Jefferson, third President of the United States of America.

On the map the Pacific Coast was plainly marked. The mouth of the Columbia was there, and the course of the great river was charted inland as far as the first mountains. East of these mountains a wilderness marked "Unknown" extended to the Rockies. The center of the continent, spangled by the Mississippi and its tributaries, was labeled "Louisiana."

Jefferson indicated the latter area smilingly.

"Our map is out of date, gentlemen. I've just heard from Mr. Livingston in Paris. He's done a fine stroke of business with Napoleon."

"You mean, Mr. President, that we've got New Orleans at last? Napoleon has signed the treaty?"

"It's more than New Orleans," Jefferson said simply. "Napoleon has offered to sell us the whole of Louisiana for sixty million francs. . . . He *has* sold it to us, I should say. Livingston accepted the offer."

"But, Mr. President—*sixty* million francs!"

"Sir, that's more than eleven million dollars! Can we afford it?"

"Can we afford not to buy six hundred million acres—at two cents an acre?" Jefferson countered. "You're missing the point, gentlemen. Today, if Congress approves what Livingston's done, we become a world power. Look again at the map. Our border is now at the Rocky Mountains. Must we stop there? Is there nothing of promise beyond?"

"You're right, Mr. President! . . . The Oregon Country! The Pacific!"

"Precisely. And we shall take steps in that direction, gentlemen."

It was called the Louisiana Purchase—the most important single event in United States history. It was the greatest single real estate transaction in the history of the world. It gave this nation title to the richest river basin on the globe's surface.

The next year Jefferson sent the Lewis and Clark Expedition across the continent to explore the Columbia to the sea. After many hardships they reached the Pacific in 1805. Their report confirmed all the legends about the extent and richness of the Columbia basin.

News of the Lewis and Clark Expedition aroused the British fur traders in the North. That the United States had acquired the vast Mississippi Valley was galling enough. That they still had designs on the Columbia was almost intolerable.

At a meeting of the Northwest Company partners in Montreal in 1808 the matter came to a head.

"Gentlemen, here is David Thompson, our agent from the Athabaska. He has a plan to propose—— Will you explain it, Thompson?"

"It's very simple, sirs. I would like to explore south through the Idaho Country, building forts along the way. By next year, or the next, I should be on the upper waters of the Columbia. I would leave some of my men there to build a

16

fort while I took my best canoemen and hurried down-river to the Pacific."

"Why not build forts on the way down the Columbia?"

"Because, sir, we must be first at the mouth of the river. That gives the Company control over the entire basin. I realize this will not please our friends, the Hudson's Bay. Nor the Yankees—who very obligingly explored the river for us."

The partners agreed to the venture, and the next year David Thompson was across the Rockies. By 1810 his string of forts had reached the Idaho Country. His progress pleased the partners in Montreal. Furs were moving across the new route. The next summer should see Thompson on the Columbia itself. It appeared that the Hudson's Bay Company—and the Americans—had been left far behind.

Then the partners got a strange letter from a New York merchant, a fur trader. The writer was their chief American competitor: John Jacob Astor. Like most of these incredible Yankees, Astor had started with nothing. He had been a butcher boy in Germany, of a poor family. He had migrated to America after the Revolution and overnight, so it seemed, had become a rival of the old and strongly entrenched British companies.

Astor's methods were completely puzzling. The British theory was to proceed cautiously. Take no chances. Profit by your opponents' mistakes. Astor was like a daring gambler who "shoots at the moon." Take a chance! If the stakes are big, take big risks. If wiped out, get together new capital and bet again. The game's the thing!

It was a new theory in world commerce, bewildering to Old Country merchants. *It was the American theory.*

This buccaneer code was soon to prove itself in sea-borne commerce, when American clipper ships became the fastest afloat, manned by the world's most daring seamen. More than one British flotilla, riding out a storm off an Atlantic port, saw one of these incredible clippers emerge from the very teeth of the gale—all sails set, its lee rail awash. It would knife on by, its canvas booming, its grinning crew clinging to the thrumming shrouds. Then it would fade into the wind-driven mists like some rollicking fragment of the storm. "Shoot at the moon!" these rustic Vikings seemed to challenge. "Let 'er go, Gallagher!"

It was more than a theory. A new figure had appeared on the world stage. The spirit of the American trader, the American clipper, and the American pioneer had begun its imprint on history. In less than a century it was to gain and envelop half a continent, dominate a hemisphere, and produce the most powerful and prosperous nation on earth.

That was the spirit of the letter received by the Northwest partners in Montreal. They were both puzzled and annoyed.

"This is preposterous, gentlemen! Who is this man Astor to make such a proposal to us? A line of forts across the continent! Control of the Columbia! Ships supplying the Russians and engaging in the China trade! . . . The man's mad."

"He invites *us* to become partners with him? When our forts are already beyond the Rockies? Disregard the letter. It's sheer impudence!"

A more cautious partner sounded a warning. "Wait, gentlemen. He asks us to send agents down to discuss it. Two of us should go. We'll pretend to treat the matter seriously—dally with it, postpone our decision. We need time."

"Time for what?"

"To send a man to warn David Thompson of Astor's scheme. We must direct Thompson to hurry down the Columbia next spring without fail—and build our fort at the mouth of the river."

"Of course! Then we'll have it! . . . But is this chap Astor to be taken that seriously?"

"One never knows about these Yankees. They say Astor

pretends he never gambles. He calls his wild schemes 'investments.' We must guard against 'investments' on the Columbia."

Two impressive visitors presently appeared in bustling New York. They were correctly dressed, their beaver top hats glistening, their gloves and morning coats immaculate. They hired a carriage and drove down to Astor's business address.

They were amazed at the appearance of the place: a big, rambling warehouse with no formal front office, no reception room or secretaries. Beyond a long counter was a busy storeroom filled to the rafters with furs, tea, teakwood, trade goods. Beyond the counter a busy little man was checking a bale of furs. He was short, stocky, with an honest, resolute face. A leather apron bulged over his plain street clothes.

The Englishmen couldn't believe this was Astor's headquarters.

"I say—can you direct us to the office of Mr. John Jacob Astor?"

"Just a minute, my friends." The little man spoke briskly, with a touch of German accent. "Just a minute, please."

He finished his checking, then took off his apron and came to the counter.

"I am sorry to keep you waiting. Now, what can I do for you?"

"But—are you Mr. Astor?"

"Yes. . . . Ah, you are from the Northwest Company. I can tell from your fine clothes. I am glad to see you. What do you think of my plan in the Pacific? It is good, no?"

"You wish to discuss it here? Our carriage is outside. Perhaps——"

"Oh no," the little man said affably. "You are busy men. I am busy. You have already made up your minds. The main question is, do you wish to be partners with me or not?"

"There are many considerations, Mr. Astor. It is an attrac-

19

tive proposal to us, but its scope is so enormous that we must proceed cautiously."

When the partners left Astor they were sure he was convinced that they meant to do business. But Astor knew men. . . . That night at the plain Astor home at 213 Broadway— where the magnificent Astor House was later built—he sat relaxed in his favorite armchair, smoking his pipe, listening to his wife playing the piano.

She stopped playing suddenly. "John, don't sit there brooding. I'm glad that crazy scheme of yours fell through. It was too big. It was much too risky. There are safer ways to make money."

"It is not the money altogether," Astor said. "Sarah, would you play a special piece for me, please? 'Tannenbaum,' eh?"

She began to play, then stopped again and turned to study his face.

"John, each time you ask me to play that, you're getting ready for a bigger gamble than ever! What is it?"

"I do not gamble. I make investments."

"Call it what you like, but out with it! What are you up to? Didn't you tell me those Montreal men weren't going through with it?"

Astor nodded. "They pretended to be willing to be partners with me, but they have made up their minds. So—I must do it alone."

"Alone? Buy ships? Build forts? Send expeditions across the continent? Why, it'll take half our fortune! . . . You haven't made up your mind?"

"Yes," Astor said. He spoke a little diffidently. "It is more than investment, Sarah. This is my country. It will be more than Astor's Fort at the mouth of the Columbia. Above it will fly the American flag. . . . I have talked to Mr. Jefferson and Mr. Madison. They give me their moral support."

"Moral support! It will cost fifty thousand dollars!"

"Four hundred thousand, my dear. . . . Now—'Tannen-baum,' eh?"

Astor's scheme was one of the boldest in the history of commerce: a singlehanded bid for empire. He bought and equipped a stout ship, the *Tonquin*. In command he placed Lieutenant Jonathan Thorne, late of the United States Navy, and started him off around the Horn. He equipped an over-land party, under command of Wilson Hunt, and started it westward from St. Louis.

Astor knew that David Thompson of the Northwest Company was somewhere in the Rockies. It was a race for the Pacific. The *Tonquin* or the overland party *might* be first at the mouth of the Columbia.

Having made his giant wager, Astor could do nothing but wait—and hope. The fall of 1810 passed—winter—the spring of 1811. There was no news, no whisper from the West.

Beyond the Rockies, as the summer of 1811 strengthened, Shoshones on the high plateau saw strange craft speeding down the sunlit current of the Columbia. They were French-Canadian bateaux—broad-beamed, sturdy boats made of whipsawed lumber. White men were aboard, singing to the beat of their flashing paddles. David Thompson and his Northwest *voyageurs* were on their way to the Pacific.

Those were glorious days for David Thompson as his bateaux sped down through the Shoshone country, past the junction of the Snake, and on into the Columbia gorge. Once they reached the sea and built a fort there, who could challenge Northwest's control of the Columbia? Who could challenge British claims to the Oregon Country?

They emerged from the gorge, singing, and paddled on through the evergreen land. Then, as they swung around the last bend, with the keen, clean breath of the Pacific blowing upon them . . .

"Wait, men! What's that ahead, there on the point? That's no Indian village!"

"It is a fort, M'sieu Thompson! A flag is flying!"

"Aye—but whose flag? . . . Look—a white man in a canoe. Close alongshore yonder . . . Halloo-o there! Whose fort down below?"

The distant canoeman answered: "Astor's Fort. John Jacob Astor of New York . . ."

"Astor!" David Thompson whispered. "There you have it, men. We've come a thousand miles down the river and what do we find? An American flag!"

Yes, the *Tonquin* had arrived safely—and first. Astor's Fort was completed. The *Tonquin* herself was gone on a trading expedition—farther up the coast, where she was later lost. But Astor's Fort commanded the bay, dominated the great river.

Thompson and his crew sadly began their long return trip. A worse chore awaited at the end: to send this bad news to Montreal.

Late that winter Wilson Hunt and the remnants of his exhausted party arrived over the overland route. This meant more men at Astoria. Another Astor ship, the *Beaver*, arrived from New York. Hunt took the *Beaver* north to trade with the Russians. Other parties moved up the Columbia to set up trading posts. For a time it seemed that Astor's great wager had won.

Fate—and the British—decreed otherwise. The War of 1812 broke out. In Montreal the Northwest Company partners at once played the trump card of global gamblers.

"Gentlemen, you will be interested to learn that I have just heard from London. They have granted our request and are sending a man-o'-war around the Horn to the Columbia."

"Ah, they'll toss those Yankees out?"

"They'll 'protect British interests.' But we have some interests to protect, gentlemen. We can't have the Hudson's

Bay snatching this plum from us. We must send McTavish
out to the Columbia at once. He may be able to manage a
spot of business for us before the man-o'-war arrives."

Now came the one hazard against which Astor had no
defense. It was what gamblers call the "double cross." Astor's
most dependable man, Hunt, was still in the North when
McTavish arrived at Astor's Fort. In command, representing
Astor, was a man named McDougall.

McDougall and McTavish soon found they had more in
common than a Scotch brogue.

"Use your head, McDougall. Isn't it better to realize something for the fort and the furs you've got than to have them
taken by force? Well, then, sell the fort to us—to the Northwest Company. Before the man-o'-war comes."

"Hm-m. Sell it, eh?"

"Exactly, man. The Company will treat you right. Didn't
Astor tell you to use your best judgment? . . . But it must be
a fair price, McDougall."

The price, naturally, was low. When the British man-o'-
war arrived the British flag was already flying over Astoria.
The owners were the Northwest Company of Montreal. The
name of the new manager was McDougall.

Thus Astor's great plan—so tremendous in scope, so close
to success—was completely destroyed. He had lost half his
fortune. The British were in control of the Columbia.

Astor heard the news one summer night, just before he and
his wife went to the theater. He sat through the performance
as though he enjoyed it thoroughly. But later, when he had
settled himself again in his armchair, pipe in hand, listening
to his wife at the piano . . .

"Sarah . . ."

"Yes? What is it, John?"

"I have just heard from one of my men at St. Louis. He
came from my fort on the Columbia. There *was* a fort, Sarah

23

—a good fort. But it is gone. The British took it over. The Northwest Company has it. . . . So we are finished on the Columbia."

"Oh, John! And the *Tonquin?*"

"Lost. Up in the North the Indians destroyed her."

"The *Beaver?*"

"In China, hiding out until the war is over. The costs in those ports will eat her up. There is nothing left of my big scheme—nothing. . . . So you may laugh, Sarah. Tell me what a fool I am. Tell me it was not an investment but a gamble. Tell me how you told me it was not an investment but a gamble. Tell me it was crazy from the beginning, that I dreamed too big! Only quickly, my dear."

She sat silent for a moment, then turned back to the piano and began to play softly. "Tannenbaum" . . . "Are you listening, John? Do you understand?"

The bowed figure straightened a little. "So—it was not a gamble, then?"

"You never bet, John."

"It was an investment which, unfortunately, failed?"

"Of course. Must we always win?"

Astor's voice grew stronger. "You are right! I have capital left. It is a big country. It is our country. In it, always, a new game begins. So—we bet again!"

"*Bet,* John?"

"No, no, I invest again. It is an investment always. An investment in the future!" Astor laughed. "You are a good wife, Sarah. . . ."

Astor's great venture failed, but the fact that the American flag had flown even briefly over his fort gave added weight to America's prior claim of discovery. The treaty of 1818 conceded equal rights in the Oregon Country to the United States. In the British view this was merely a diplomatic expedient. They were actually in possession of the disputed ground. "What we have, v. old."

Events proved Britain's error. The boldness of Gray, the foresight of Thomas Jefferson, and Astor's buccaneer gesture had planted the seeds of a mighty harvest.

1813 – 1828

The slow-moving but inexorable Hudson's Bay soon swallowed up the Northwest Company and assumed control of Astor's Fort at the mouth of the Columbia. In 1824 they moved their headquarters eighty miles upriver to Fort Vancouver. In command as Chief Factor was Dr. John McLoughlin, destined to become one of the region's immortals.

Dr. McLoughlin ruled the only feudal state ever to appear in America. Fort Vancouver became the center of an empire of 470,000 square miles. It extended from California to Alaska and from the Rockies to the Pacific, a land area greater than that of today's England, France, Belgium, and Germany.

Over this immense region Dr. McLoughlin—known to the Indians as the White-Headed Eagle—ruled with an iron hand: benevolently but with absolute authority. He had two aims: to defend the Hudson's Bay Company's fur monopoly against all comers and particularly the Yankees, and to keep the British flag flying over the Oregon Country. He did so successfully for twenty-two years.

In the end he failed. On several dramatic occasions the doctor himself saw the undermining forces at work, like tiny trickles of water weakening the foundations of a mighty dam.

III

THE SAGA OF LOUIS LA BONTE

A FINE spring morning in 1828 found Dr. John McLoughlin, Chief Factor, busy at his desk at Fort Vancouver, the Hudson's Bay Company's most westerly post on the North American continent.

The fort stood on a rise of ground on the north bank of the Columbia River. It covered about two acres enclosed in a split-log palisade. Two brass cannon, formidable in appearance but used only on state occasions, made the great gate impressive. A sentry walked there, his musket sloping.

Within the enclosure were living quarters for the army of Company officers and clerks and huge warehouses for furs and supplies. In the center was the two-story headquarters of Dr. John McLoughlin, where all state functions were held and all business transacted. Above it flew the British flag and the house emblem of Hudson's Bay.

The doctor was a tall, powerfully built man of commanding appearance. He was a born despot, a ruler, a man of violent moods. Sometimes he came to the desk with the temper of a grizzly bear, but this morning he was in a fine good humor. A beautiful day was in prospect, and all was well in the empire.

It was true that a Yankee ship, the *Owyhee,* was anchored a short distance downstream, attempting to trade with the near-by Multnomahs, but this merely added zest to the doctor's mood. He knew how to deal with the Yankees. Everything was under control.

His chief clerk, Alexander McLeod, stood dourly by the desk.

"Well, McLeod, we're in fine shape! I've a good report from the Spokane House and Walla Walla. And we seem to have the best of those Yankees up on the Snake. They'll soon starve out! So we're free to concentrate on this Captain Dimick—Dammack—what *is* that infernal Yankee's name?"

"Captain Dominis, sir. . . . And I'm a bit worried about him. He's likely to get furs."

"He'll get nothing from the Multnomahs! Young Chief Casseno's assured me of that. And the Chinooks will have nothing to do with him. Chief Comcomly's our friend. I've warned the whole river not to trade with the Boston men. So where will this Dominkis get furs?"

"*Dominis,* sir. . . . Casseno's afraid he can't keep some of his men from trading privately with the Yankees. Captain Dominis is offering one blanket for *four* beaver skins instead of six. One musket for fifteen beaver instead of twenty."

"What?" the doctor shouted. "So that's his game, eh? He'll try to cut the throats of the Hudson's Bay, will he? Better men than Dimkus have tried that, McLeod! Send word to Casseno that we're giving a blanket for *two* beaver. A musket for ten. How's that, eh?"

McLeod was staggered. "It will ruin the Yankees, but what about us? After the *Owyhee's* gone and the Indians are accustomed to such outrageous prices——"

"Get rid of them first! We'll set our own prices later! These infernal Yankees . . ." Abruptly the doctor's irritation faded. "Well, McLeod, nothing else? Come, let's go out and watch them plowing. Think of it—we'll soon be raising our own wheat, corn, and potatoes! Enough for us and all the up-river forts! . . . Don't look so gloomy, man! Forget the Yankees. We'll soon run this Dimmis off the river!"

"*Dominis,* sir."

"Bah!"

The doctor strode out the great gate with McLeod at his side. McLeod was a big man, but the White-Headed Eagle towered above him: he was six feet four and walked erectly, his white hair flowing over his broad shoulders. His hair was prematurely white; he was actually less than fifty, in the prime of life.

He strode like a conqueror, twirling his gold-headed cane, and the Indians outside the gate stood back respectfully as the great man passed by.

"Ah—look at the rich soil they're turning up! You can tell it's rich by the smell of it. What a day, McLeod, what a day! Let's go down by the river. . . . Look—some of our boys are just starting out. Where to?"

"To Celilo, sir."

"There's color, man! There's drama! Open up your Scotch heart and enjoy it! Look at those paddles flashing! Listen to them sing! Beautiful, beautiful . . ." The doctor glanced back over his shoulder. "Who's that man, McLeod? He followed us down from the fort. Isn't that La Bonte—Louis la Bonte?"

"Yes," McLeod said, annoyed. "I warned him not to bother you."

"It's all right. He's a good lad. But I've already said good-by to him. I've given him a fine letter to Montreal. I've given him a good bonus. What else does he want?"

"It's of no importance, sir. I'll give him a piece of my mind."

"Wait—it may be important to *him*, McLeod. He's served the Company faithfully. . . . All right, La Bonte! Step up here!"

"Yes, m'sieu." La Bonte came closer, timidly. He was a swarthy giant with black, liquid eyes. His manner toward McLoughlin was that of a frightened boy approaching a formidable schoolmaster. "I do not wish, m'sieu—I am sorry to trouble you——"

31

"Well, what is it? How's that fine boy of yours—Louis, isn't it? Louis must be all of six years old now, eh?"

"Eight, m'sieu. Yes, he is a fine boy."

"And your good squaw—Klick-Tosh?"

"Kil-akot-ah, m'sieu. Yes, she is fine—but very sad because I must leave for Montreal." La Bonte twisted his red *voyageur's* cap in his enormous hands. Perspiration glistened on his face. "That is what I wish to talk about, *M'sieu le Facteur*. Must I go to Montreal for my discharge? Could you not give it to me here, so I could stay in the country?"

"What? Stay *here* after you're discharged? You want to live with your squaw's tribe? You wouldn't like that, La Bonte."

"No, m'sieu, I want to take my squaw and my boy Louis and settle in the Willamette Valley." La Bonte gestured humbly toward the south. "There is a beautiful place by the river where I could build my cabin. It is the place by the river that is called Champoeg."

"You want to go to farming over there? Impossible, La Bonte! It's against the Company rules. You'll have to get your discharge in Montreal."

"But, m'sieu——"

"On your way now!" McLeod broke in. "Are you arguing with the doctor?"

"No, m'sieu." La Bonte turned and shambled away.

The doctor went on, muttering: "What notions these *habitants* get! A trapper, a Company man, wanting to settle in the Willamette Valley!" He looked out across the Columbia toward the south. In that direction the plumed timber dwindled as into the vastness of a shoreless sea. "You know, McLeod, that must be a beautiful valley. I'll have to take a trip down there when I have more time."

"It is beautiful, sir. The Shoshones call it 'the land of plenty.' It might be good farming, at that."

"This is *fur* country, McLeod! Never forget it! Let all Company men remember it!"

"Right, sir."

The doctor went about his affairs and forgot La Bonte. French Canadians were like happy children—volatile, naïve, usually incapable of deep or lasting feelings. Each Company man had entered service in Montreal. Their contract over, they must return to Montreal for their discharge and bonus. The Hudson's Bay control of the Oregon Country was absolute. They wanted no footloose white men prowling their empire.

La Bonte knew this rule. It was more than a rule; it was law. Late that night, when the stars were flaming above the Columbia, he and his squaw sat beside their fire in the Indian camp west of the fort, considering their future. Their little boy was asleep in the near-by tent. Except for the occasional rattle of a musket at the gate of the fort, where the sentry walked his lonely post, the night was still.

Kil-akot-ah—"Little Songbird"—was a young and handsome woman, the daughter of a minor chief of the Chinooks. La Bonte had never learned the Chinook jargon, but his squaw had mastered the white man's tongue. She dared not speak now until her lord and master had reached his decision.

La Bonte spoke suddenly:

"It is final, *p'tite*—you cannot go to Montreal with me. The winters are too cold. The people are strange. This is your country."

"Then stay here, Louis," she said in a low voice. "Come with me to my tribe. My father is Comcomly's right-hand man. Comcomly will protect us."

"No. The White-Headed Eagle is a greater chief than Comcomly. It would only make trouble for your tribe. I must go to Montreal to get my discharge. But I will come back, *p'tite*."

"All that long, weary way?" She bowed her head hopelessly to her knees. "No, you will drown in the rapids. You will be lost in the deep snow of the mountains. Out on the great plains you will die of thirst."

"Not I," said La Bonte.

"Besides, your people are in Montreal. Why should you come back? No white man who has gone to get his discharge has ever returned. You will forget Kil-akot-ah. You will find some young and beautiful white woman there, one of whom you will not be ashamed——"

"Hush," La Bonte said. "It is far to Montreal—so far that two winters will pass before I see you again. So remember what I tell you now. . . . I have seen no country more beautiful than the valley of the Willamette. I shall meet no finer woman than you, *chérie*. There are no rapids, nor deep snows, nor deserts that can stop Louis la Bonte. . . . So wait for me. Keep your campfire burning. Do not lose heart. *I will be back.*"

It attracted no notice at the fort when La Bonte left with the upriver flotilla. He was just another trapper homeward bound, his term of service done. A few of his companions were there to say good-by. A squaw and little one—as usual on such an occasion—were left weeping on the bank.

Big events went forward that summer at the fort. The downriver express arrived from Fort Spokane with splendid furs. The Yankees were driven from the Snake. There was talk of building forts up on Puget Sound and even farther north.

The Yankee ship, *Owyhee,* was still on the river next spring. Captain Dominis, a stubborn man, offered a musket for eight beaver skins, and the doctor roared at Casseno and Comcomly that the Company price was now *five* beaver for one musket—an unheard-of thing in the Northwest trade.

That summer a still greater burden came to the doctor.

A terrible epidemic broke out among the Indians along the river: a fever and ague which touched white men only lightly but caused native men, women, and children to die like flies. Louis la Bonte's squaw and little one survived, but the death chant rose up in fifty villages between the Cascades and the sea.

Sick ones flocked to the fort, knowing the White-Headed Eagle was a great man of medicine, but the epidemic raged on. The Indians sought an explanation for this frightful calamity—and finally found it. One day the doctor came back to the fort in a towering rage. He stamped into the office, roaring like an angry bull.

"McLeod! Where are ye, man!"

McLeod came running. "Here, sir. What's wrong, Doctor?"

"What's wrong, he says! A fine kettle of fish! McLeod, who started this story among the Indians?"

"What story?"

"That this epidemic is the fault of the Yankees! That the Boston men opened up a bottle and poured out the sickness! Who's responsible for it, eh?"

"I've heard the story, sir." McLeod was evasive. "I shouldn't think you'd object. After all, if we can turn the Indians against the Yankees——"

"Listen, you numskull! I'll fight the Yankees tooth and nail! I'll rip the shirts from their backs! I'll hound them out of the country with a forked stick—but I'll do it fair and decent! If I cut a man's throat I'll do it to his face!"

"But, Doctor——"

"There'll be no massacre of white men on this river!" the doctor thundered. "I'll see no blood spilled! We've got obligations, man! Send messengers up and down the river to tell the Indians that this fool story's wrong. Tell them that the Boston men and King George men both want their furs—but neither of them will harm the Indians. D'ye hear?"

"Yes, sir."

"A fine business! We must preserve our dignity, McLeod. What will this man Dimmis be thinking of us?"

"*Dominis*, sir."

"Get out of here!"

It was too late to stop the story once it was started. There might have been serious trouble for the *Owyhee* and its Yankee crew except that another story spread like wildfire down the river.

It started at the *Owyhee,* which was anchored off the mouth of the Willamette, just below the fort. One morning the alarm sounded and Captain Dominis rushed out on deck to find the *Owyhee* surrounded by war canoes filled with angry Multnomahs.

But the *Owyhee's* half-breed interpreter was grinning. "They say, Captain, that this sickness is your fault."

"*My* fault!" echoed the hard-bitten Dominis. "Why?"

"They've been told you have a bottle full of evil medicine —and that you opened this bottle and poured death on the river."

"Who told them that? Hm-m. McLoughlin, eh? Two can play at that game! Tell those savages it wasn't the Boston men who caused the sickness. It was the King George men themselves—as a punishment for selling us salmon and furs."

The interpreter was doubtful. "But will they believe it? It must sound reasonable."

"Make it reasonable! They've plowed some ground over at the fort, haven't they? Wasn't it the first time ground was plowed in these parts? There you have it. The sickness was in the ground, and when they broke the ground they let the sickness out. . . ."

This counterpropaganda so bewildered the Indians that their war councils were divided and no plans could be agreed upon. Fortunately the epidemic passed its peak, though it continued to ravage scattered villages. The stopping of trade proved too much for Dominis. Early that summer the *Owyhee* sailed downstream and the Columbia saw her no more.

The business of the empire went on. There were other brushes with Yankee traders, but the doctor was invincible. Trouble with Clatsop and Puget Sound tribes was soon smoothed over. The Indians were learning to respect the doctor above all other men. He was stern, but he was also just. He punished the wrongdoer and rewarded those who were honest and trustworthy. Above all, he never broke a promise.

By midsummer the empire was stronger than ever. Not a cloud was in the sky. The doctor was at his desk alone one morning, working on his papers in fine good humor, when a shadow fell across the doorway.

"Is that you, McLeod?" the doctor asked without looking up. "What can I do for you, McLeod? You've found something to worry about, ye long-faced deacon?"

A shy voice said: "Good morning, *M'sieu le Facteur.*"

"Well, Louis! How are you? How's that fine boy——*Louis la Bonte!*" The doctor sat back, scowling. "What are you doing here? I thought you went to Montreal a couple of years ago?"

"I did, m'sieu. And I have come back again."

"So I see," the doctor said grimly. "Why?"

"To take my family to the Willamette Valley," La Bonte said with humility. "To the place called Champoeg. With your permission, m'sieu——I have my discharge from the Company," he hurried on. "I am a free man now. If you will let me have the few supplies that I need I will pay you back after I have had time——"

"That's enough!" the doctor roared. "Sell him a few supplies, he says! Didn't I warn you not to come back here? McLeod!"

"Coming, sir." McLeod hurried in and stopped short at sight of La Bonte. "Well, La Bonte, what's the meaning of this? What did you come back for?"

"To take his family down to the valley," the doctor mimicked. "To the place called Champoeg. Bah! What shall we do with him, McLeod?"

"He knows the Company rule. He came back in spite of it. We'll lock him up. Send him back in irons on the first ship. . . . Come along, La Bonte."

"Wait, m'sieu," La Bonte pleaded desperately. "It is not much that I ask. My squaw has waited for me. My boy is much bigger now—a fine boy. I do not use much land in the valley. It is a big valley. I do not frighten away the beaver——"

"Stop!" McLeod cut in. "Didn't you hear the doctor? Do I have to call the guard?"

"No, m'sieu."

"Wait," the doctor said. "Wait, McLeod. Let's look into this."

He sat back, his formidable eyes fixed upon La Bonte. He knew every mile of the overland trail to Montreal. Beyond this trembling giant he saw the weary width of the continent.

"La Bonte," he said, "how did you get to Montreal?"

"First I go up the river past the Spokane House. To the last portage."

The doctor nodded. "Eight hundred miles. Hard paddling, was it?"

"Only in the rapids. Then I go over the mountains."

"Ah yes," the doctor said, stroking his jaw. "The Rockies. It was winter then. The snow was deep, eh?"

"Yes, but I wore the snowshoes. Then I go to Fort William, on Lake Superior."

"Eighteen hundred miles. It was summer by that time. You did a lot of walking. Hot, was it?"

"There was some dust and wind," La Bonte admitted. "Not too bad. Then down the lakes and the St. Lawrence——"

"And back again," the doctor said. "Eight thousand miles

altogether. It took you two years. . . . Why did you do it, La Bonte?"

"Well"—La Bonte twisted his hat in his great hands—"to take my family down to the valley——"

"To that place called Champoeg! I know." The doctor scowled and cleared his throat. "La Bonte, d'ye know what I'm going to do with you?"

"Please, m'sieu——" La Bonte began.

"Quiet! I'm going to give you credit for whatever you need. Not too much, mind you—it has to be paid back. I'm going to send one of the bateaux with a couple of the men to lend a hand. I understand there's a falls you have to portage."

"M'sieu!" La Bonte whispered, overwhelmed. "Heaven will bless you! *Le bon Dieu*——"

"Never mind, never mind!" the doctor said testily. "When do you want to start? Right away, I suppose?"

"We are ready to go, m'sieu."

"Take care of him McLeod. Get a couple of the boys."

"But, Doctor, I must say——"

"Say nothing, ye long-faced ape!" the doctor roared. "Can't you see I'm a busy man? Start him off!"

"Yes, sir. . . . Come along, La Bonte."

Left alone, the doctor took up his pen, scowling. "There's always something!" he muttered. "These infernal details!" His pen scratched. "*Eight thousand* miles! Who can fight that sort of thing, Company rules or not? Though it probably outweighs all the victories we've had over the Yankees. The first Company man to settle in the valley. On the *land*, McLoughlin! There'll be others." He paused in his writing to look out through the open door and across the Columbia southward. "We must go down and look at the valley someday. I've no doubt it's a bonny sight. Particularly that place called Champoeg."

1828 – 1829

In the fall of 1828 Dr. John McLoughlin, Chief Factor at Fort Vancouver, was preparing to receive a distinguished visitor. He was more than a mere visitor: he was the only living man from whom the doctor had to take orders—George Simpson, governor of the Hudson's Bay Company in North America.

Knowing Governor Simpson, the doctor was a little worried about the impending visit. He did not fear inspection of the Oregon Country. Enormous quantities of furs were moving through the fort. The Company's rule was absolute from California to Alaska. The doctor was proud of his accomplishments.

What he feared was Governor Simpson's lack of understanding of the problems of the frontier. Simpson was stiff, British, a little pompous. He thought all Indians were bad Indians. He despised the Americans. A wrong word or gesture could easily be misinterpreted at Fort Vancouver.

The doctor's fears were well founded. Simpson's slight to a soft-spoken American trapper affected the course of history west of the Rocky Mountains.

IV

GENTLEMAN FROM THE SOUTH

THE visit of George Simpson, governor of the Hudson's Bay Company, was an event of first importance at Fort Vancouver in the fall of 1828. It called for weeks of preparation. The accounts must be in order, the inventory of furs and equipment up to date. A detailed history of the Company's activities during the preceding four years must be available.

Dr. John McLoughlin and his gloomy chief clerk, Alexander McLeod, worked late each night at the doctor's headquarters. McLeod had drawn a large map of the area showing the Company's principal establishments in the Oregon Country, with historical notes attached. One night in early August he spread it on the desk for the doctor's inspection.

The doctor was pleased. It was a graphic record of success.

"Not bad, McLeod! Not bad! We've spread out in the past four years, eh?"

"The governor will give us no credit for it," McLeod predicted.

"No, he'll compliment us. Give the devil his due. . . . Hm-m. You haven't marked the Clellum battle?"

"It seemed best to omit it, sir. The less said about that unfortunate business, the better."

"Nonsense! We've got nothing to hide. Those Clellums killed five of our men in cold blood. Aye, good men. We had to punish them. White men must be able to travel in safety in the Oregon Country."

"Even Americans?" said McLeod with a gloomy twinkle.

"Of course! Well, mark it down, then we're off to bed. You know, McLeod, I get along fine with these infernal Yankees. In fact, I like them. I'd cut their throats in a business way. They'd cut mine. We understand each other—and remain friends. I'm afraid Governor Simpson won't understand that."

"Correct, sir."

"Fortunately," the doctor said, yawning, "there isn't a Yankee in the country. So the governor shouldn't be annoyed."

The doctor was wrong. Late that very night there was an uproar at the gate. The sentry shouted his challenge. Dogs barked. The whole fort was aroused. The doctor put on a dressing gown, lighted a candle, and hurried downstairs.

McLeod rushed in. "What is it, sir? What's happening?"

"Go and find out, ye numskull! Wait—here they come. What have you got there, sentry?"

"An American, sir. He says he escaped from the Indians down south."

The crowd halted at the office door. Two clerks were half supporting, half carrying an emaciated white man. His clothing was in tatters, and his head hung with weakness.

"He's in bad shape, Doctor. What shall we do with him?"

"Bring him in!" the doctor roared. "Lend a hand there! My word, McLeod, the poor fellow's practically skin and bones. He needs food. He needs medical attention."

"And he needs a bath," McLeod said fastidiously. "Shall we make a bed for him in the square?"

"Carry him up to the guest room, ye dim-wit! Get the servants up. Have them heat water. Get some food ready!"

After the Yankee was cared for the doctor sat beside his bed and listened to his story.

The Yankee's name was Black. He was one of a party of

traders headed by Jedediah Smith of the Rocky Mountain Fur Company. They had explored southwest to California and on their way north had been ambushed by the Umpqua Indians. Captain Smith and two other men had been away from camp when the attack came, and Black was sure they, too, had been killed. Black had escaped into the forest and had made his way along the coast on foot.

The doctor was aroused at once. He assured Black that the Umpqua Indians would be punished and the furs and horses the party had lost would be recovered, if possible. This promise puzzled McLeod when they discussed it downstairs.

"You don't really mean it, sir—about sending an armed party tomorrow to punish the Umpquas?"

"Certainly I meant it. Why not?"

"They were Yankee traders. It might be good business to let the Umpquas know—privately, you understand——"

"Shame on ye, McLeod! The Yankees are entitled to protection. We'd expect it of them if *they* controlled the country! This Jedediah Smith may have escaped. If so, you must save him."

"I?"

"Yes—you, McLeod! You'll start tomorrow with thirty picked men. You'll start south and keep going until you come to the Umpqua. When you meet those reptiles—but I'll give you instructions in the morning."

The next day, before McLeod started south with his army, Jedediah Smith and his two companions appeared at the fort. They, too, had escaped the Umpquas by a narrow margin. They were in terrible condition—barely able to stand. The doctor put them to bed to recuperate and started McLeod south with his avenging army.

While McLeod was gone the doctor and Jedediah Smith got well acquainted. Each had heard of the other but had never before met. Jedediah Smith was one of the most daring of Yankee explorers, the first fur trader to cross the Sierras into California. He was a tall, easygoing man; a native of Boston but a true frontiersman now. He was—by contrast with most Yankee traders—a deeply religious man. The doctor liked him on sight.

The Americans were overwhelmed by the doctor's hospitality. They were treated like kings. Nothing was said about paying for their food, lodging, and medical care.

And when McLeod returned from the Umpqua expedition with all their furs, horses, and equipment, nothing was said about that. Their forty horses were turned in with the Company horses. Their 702 beaver skins were merely added to the Company's furs.

The four Americans discussed their situation cautiously one day as they sat in the warm sunshine outside the gate of the fort.

"Jed," one of them queried, "you reckon we're afoot or horseback?"

"Looks like we're afoot," Jed returned.

"What about our furs?"

"I wouldn't know," Jed said. His calm eyes twinkled a little. "When we were swimming across the Umpqua with those arrows falling around us like hail, I prayed to God to get *us* out of trouble. I didn't mention furs."

"But they got them back. We'd ought to get something out of those furs."

Jed turned to Black at his right. "How about it, Black? When you came crawling up to the fort that night, with your bones showing through your skin, did *you* figure on doing any horse trading?"

"Not me!" Black said with conviction. "When all those other memories are growing dim, I'll still remember what the doctor said. I figured he'd yell: 'One of those Yankees? Throw him out! Let the Indians have him!'"

"What *did* he say?"

"He said—and he was tough about it: 'Bring him in! Lend a hand there!'"

Jed chuckled. "It's pleasant here in the sun, isn't it?"

But Jedediah Smith was not the man to accept hospitality —and particularly from a bitter trade rival—without coming to some understanding about it. One day the doctor looked up to see the tall, quiet Yankee standing by his desk.

"Sorry to disturb you, sir."

"Not at all! Not at all! You're looking much better, Captain Smith. But it'll be another month before you lads are on your feet." The doctor rustled through his papers briskly. "By the way, I've got your account figured out."

"That's what I wanted to discuss with you, sir."

"I know, I know. I've been terribly busy. Getting ready for Governor Simpson, you know. . . . Here you are, Captain. It's all itemized. There were 702 beaver, 40 otter. And your horses. I hope it's satisfactory. I've attached my draft on the Company for the total."

Jedediah Smith studied the account and the attached draft, deeply puzzled.

"I'm not sure I understand this, Doctor. The draft is for fourteen *thousand* dollars! You're paying us the market price for all our furs and the horses that you got back from the Umpquas?"

"Ah yes—the horses. I assumed you wanted us to take them off your hands. There's no trail over the mountains yet. Whatever you wish, of course. Was that what you meant?"

"No, sir," Jedediah said. "What I meant was that we're not entitled to any such money. We lost everything to those Umpquas, almost including our scalps. If you hadn't sent an army down there——"

"Nonsense!" the doctor cut in affably. "Certainly you're entitled to recover your property. . . . Anything else, Captain? Any complaints?"

47

"Yes, sir. You haven't subtracted anything for our food and lodging."

"What? You and your men are guests of the fort, sir!"

"You mean you're not charging us for anything? In addition to paying us for our furs? Now that isn't right, Doctor!"

"Say no more about it." The doctor brushed it aside. "By the way, the governor will soon be here. He doesn't understand Americans. I'd appreciate it if you lads would—er—make yourselves as inconspicuous as possible."

"I understand, sir. We'll move out of the fort and camp with the Indians."

"Oh no—that's unnecessary. Just mingle with the clerks and trappers. I'm sure he won't notice you."

Jedediah nodded. "But will you permit me, Doctor, on behalf of my men, to thank you most kindly——"

"It's quite all right," the doctor said hastily. "You Rocky Mountain lads would have done the same for me if I were marooned in your territory."

"*Would* we? Anyway, thank you, sir."

The doctor's generosity deeply touched the hearts of the Americans. There seemed no way to repay it. Yet they were able to make a small contribution to the social life of the fort.

One night a week, when the rainy fall weather permitted, there was community singing in the square. The doctor encouraged this for purposes of morale. Occasionally even the French-Canadian *voyageurs*, who were vagabonds at heart, felt themselves to be far from home in this lonely outpost.

On one of these "singing nights" the entire white population of the fort gathered in the square beneath the stars. The doctor stood in the lighted doorway of his office as master of ceremonies, with the dim faces of the crowd turned toward his giant, comforting figure. Many motionless Indians listened in the outer shadows, not comprehending the words but touched by the white man's haunting tribal songs.

A group of *voyageurs* sang an old chantey familiar in far-off Quebec. When the applause died, the doctor's great voice spoke with a rare touch of gentleness.

"Very fine. It takes us back to the good old St. Lawrence. I'm sorry we can't offer some American song for the benefit of our guests who are also far from their familiar ground."

Jedediah spoke softly from the edge of the crowd.

"Dr. McLoughlin . . ."

"Yes, Captain Smith?"

"It seems like we should do something for you people. There's a new hymn they're singing back in Missouri. You probably haven't heard it yet. We don't claim to be top-notch singers, but we'll try it if you like."

"Let's have it, by all means, sir."

So the four Americans sang with voices of surprising quality and harmony. The hymn was "Greenland's Icy Mountains." The crowd listened raptly and applauded with vigor.

"Good," the doctor approved. "And it's a noble sentiment. Can you oblige us with another, gentlemen?"

"We can try one which isn't a hymn," Jedediah said. "It's a song they made up down Texas way. They call it 'The Red River Valley.'"

"I'll have you know, gentlemen," the doctor said with pretended severity, "that Red River is an Athabaska river, *not* Texas." The crowd laughed heartily. "Let's have it, sirs."

The haunting refrain of this song deeply touched the emotional *voyageurs*. Many wept openly as the last words died away. In those moments they gained a greater understanding of these hard-faced, soft-spoken strangers. They were more than human wolves prowling the wilderness. The Americans, too, had land and homes they loved far away.

Governor Simpson finally arrived with great pomp and circumstance. Inspections, banquets, and conferences followed. It was now late fall, and neither the governor nor the Americans could start upriver until spring.

Jedediah and his men tried to keep out of the governor's way, but the inevitable soon happened. One day the governor was inspecting the blacksmith shop and discovered the four Americans there.

The governor was a waspish little man with a broad British accent.

"What's this, McLoughlin—*five* blacksmiths? Are so many necessary?"

"Oh no. These four are only spectators. Now, sir, if you'd like to look in at the cooperage——"

"Wait." The governor examined Jedediah with kindling suspicion. The American's manner held none of the French Canadian's awe of authority. "I say, my man, I've seen you about the fort. What is your business?"

"We're trappers, sir."

"My word—what an odd accent! What is your name? Where are you from?"

"The name's Smith, sir. We're Americans. . . . I'm sorry, Doctor."

"It's all right," the doctor said. "Yes, they're Americans, Governor. They've been recuperating here at the fort—the sole survivors of an Indian massacre."

"Really? What were the circumstances?"

"It's in my report. The Umpqua affair."

"We'll glance over the report again," the governor said. "Immediately. In your office, McLoughlin."

In the office there was a sharp clash between the governor and McLoughlin. The doctor explained that he could do nothing else than give aid to Jedediah Smith and his men. They had been at the point of death.

Moreover, the doctor insisted, it was imperative that American fur traders feel that the Company was just in its dealings. Theoretically, at least, the Americans had equal rights in the Oregon Country. Once the American public was aroused, there might be a sudden interest in the agricultural possibilities of the Willamette Valley. That, above all, was what the doctor feared.

The governor brushed these arguments aside. The Yankees had no rights west of the Rockies. Was the doctor naïve enough to believe in the face value of the Joint Occupation Treaty once the British flag had flown over the disputed ground? There would be a sharp accounting with these Yankee "guests" before he, the governor, left in the spring.

One day in early spring, just when the doctor was beginning to hope the governor had forgotten his threat, Jedediah Smith strode into the office with a voluminous letter in his hand. McLeod was there, and the doctor motioned him to stay. Jedediah's formal manner warned of an impending crisis.

"May I talk to you a moment, Doctor?"

"Of course. Of course. Sit down."

"I would like to have the governor here," Jedediah said. He remained standing. "He signed this letter."

"Disregard it, Captain," the doctor urged. "I know what's in it. It's all right."

"I won't have you embarrassed, sir," Jed insisted. "Send for the governor, please."

"Very well. Go get him, McLeod."

When McLeod was gone Jedediah looked steadily at the doctor. "Before he comes, sir, I want to tell you that you rank among the truest gentlemen I've been privileged to meet. Your Company has treated me with every kindness. I will so report to my people in the East."

The doctor rose to his feet with dignity. "Thank you, Captain."

"As a token of my personal appreciation, Doctor, I will also tell you that my company will withdraw from the Snake. We'll consider it your trading territory and stay in the Rockies."

"That's very kind of you, sir."

51

The governor arrived, frowning. "Well, what is it? Ah—it's Smith. I see you have my letter, Smith. Let me tell you at once that it's useless to argue the matter. I'll not change its terms. The doctor's offer was out of reason. Three dollars each for your beaver is ample. A total of thirty-two hundred dollars, including the horses—and quite generous, I assure you! Where else could you sell your horses?"

"Very well, sir."

"You're not haggling over it? Aren't you a bit out of the Yankee character?"

"I'm not debating the question of character, sir," Jed said. "Here is the draft you gave me, Doctor."

"*I* object, Governor!" The doctor's face flushed angrily. "As Chief Factor of this post, I made the offer in good faith."

"It's rescinded. I shall direct the head office not to honor your draft."

"And I'll report this whole affair to London!"

"Are you aware, Doctor, to whom you're talking?"

"Gentlemen!" Jedediah interposed. "Never mind, Doctor." He tore up the draft and tossed the fragments into the waste-basket. "There! Make out a new one for whatever amount is agreeable to the governor."

The doctor's flush deepened. "This is most embarrassing. I assure you, Captain——"

"It's all right, sir. You and I understand each other. Let's hear what else the governor has to say."

"Just this, my man. I hope it's quite clear that you Yankees will not be tolerated on the Columbia."

"Not *tolerated*, sir?" Jed said softly. "Are you speaking for the Hudson's Bay Company—or for the British Empire?"

"You're beyond your depth there, I think," the governor said. "But let's not quibble. We control the Oregon Country. We shall continue to do so."

"He means in a competitive way, of course," the doctor interposed.

"I think I understand his meaning," Jed said. "Doctor, you know my feelings of friendship toward you. Nothing will change that. You'll be the first to admit, however, that our personal friendship has nothing to do with our patriotism. That is correct, sir?"

"That is correct, Captain."

"This is most impressive," the governor said.

"I didn't mean to sound dramatic, Governor," Jed said. "I'll report your attitude to my people in the East. I'll tell them that it's useless to compete with the Hudson's Bay Company out here in the Oregon Country—*in the fur trade.*"

"I'm glad I made myself clear."

"But I'll recommend, sir, that the possibilities for farming out here be investigated."

"Farming? Two thousand miles from the Missouri frontier?"

"Yes, sir. It isn't generally known back there how big and beautiful the Willamette Valley is."

The governor laughed. "A quaint notion! Well, thank you, Smith. I'll toddle along, Doctor. Write out that new draft for him, eh?"

"Very well, Governor."

After the governor was gone the doctor, McLeod, and Jedediah Smith stood for a moment in silence. Then Jedediah smiled.

"Don't feel badly, Doctor. That's been on my conscience all the while. It *is* a beautiful valley. I was bound to report it."

McLeod eyed him coldly. "You're a secret agent, then? A spy?"

"I'm an American citizen, sir."

"Well said, Captain," the doctor approved. "But how do you know the valley's good farm country?"

"I saw it. I know good soil. I think I'm the first American to travel the entire length of the valley. I had to, to get here from the Umpqua. I judge it to be two hundred miles long, Doctor. There are meadows and natural prairies. I've never seen such game and wild fruit and belly-deep grass."

"That's right," the doctor said heavily. "You *saw* the valley. . . ."

After Jedediah Smith had said good night the doctor sat for a time at his desk, disregarding McLeod, his chin resting on his hands. Then he took up his pen and began to write out the new draft, his lips framing the words.

"Thirty-two hundred dollars . . . That was a bad stroke of business, laddie."

"It saved the Company more than ten thousand dollars, sir."

"And it may cost us the Oregon Country. Settlers mean the end of the fur trade. It's the weak point in our armor, McLeod."

Even McLeod's unimaginative mind was touched by the shadow on the doctor's face. The White-Headed Eagle had aged during the past hour. "It wasn't your fault, sir. It was bound to come sooner or later."

"I suppose so. . . . You saw the valley, too, McLeod. *Is* it that beautiful?"

"I doubt if there's a fairer countryside to be found on the continent."

The doctor sighed. "I must get down to see it, McLeod. This summer, *sure*. . . ."

1828 – 1834

Accounts of Jedediah Smith's adventures, circulated widely along the Eastern seaboard, stirred an imaginative Boston schoolteacher, Hall Kelley, to preach the gospel of the Oregon Country.

Kelley's zeal inflamed a young Bostonian, Nathaniel Wyeth, and a jovial adventurer, Captain Benjamin Louis E. Bonneville, to head separate trading expeditions to the Columbia in 1831 and 1832. Both ventures ended disastrously. Bonneville was discouraged, but Wyeth swore he would accumulate new capital and try again.

Dr. McLoughlin was undisturbed. His victories over Wyeth and Bonneville seemed to demonstrate anew that his position was invulnerable. The Hudson's Bay controlled the fur trade, the lifeblood of the region.

Yet a strengthening, inner voice warned the doctor that his empire's true weakness was in the south, where the vast Willamette Valley brooded. Several of the Company's ex-employees had followed Louis la Bonte and settled there with their Indian wives and children. No white man who had seen the valley ever forgot its beauty and obvious fertility.

In the summer of 1832, the affairs of the empire permitting, the doctor crossed the Columbia and made his first inspection of the region known to the Shoshones as Oyer-ungun, or "place of plenty."

V

GOOD APPLES IN THE BARREL

THOUGH he had ruled the Oregon Country from Fort Vancouver for eight years, it was not until midsummer of 1832 that Dr. John McLoughlin found time to cross the Columbia River for a personal inspection of the vast and placid valley of the Willamette.

The northern extremity of the valley was directly opposite the fort, and only a four-day expedition was involved, yet the doctor traveled in the impressive style due the Chief Factor of the Hudson's Bay Company's largest and richest empire.

In the lead were expert canoemen familiar with the currents of the Willamette River. Next came the large bateau bearing the doctor and his assistant, James Douglas, manned by a dozen colorful *voyageurs* who sang to the beat of their flashing oars. Bringing up the rear was the still larger bateau carrying the camp gear, the doctor's cook and camp tenders, and presents for the Indians and Company men.

The flotilla mounted up to the falls of the Willamette some twenty miles south of the Columbia, portaged over them, and proceeded on to the place called Champoeg, where the old Company men had settled. Here, at sundown, the doctor held the soil of the Willamette Valley in his hands and thrilled to its richness. He climbed an adjacent hill and looked south over one of the most beautiful of the continent's untouched wildernesses.

The valley was some one hundred and fifty miles long by

fifty miles wide near its central portion. Natural meadows, groves, and sparkling creeks stretched as far as the eye could see. Luxuriant vegetation and wild game were everywhere. The lofty Cascade Mountains on the east and timbered hills to the west protected this happy region both from the fogs of the coast and the cold of the interior.

This was the valley which was shortly to be known as "the land where flowers bloom at Christmas and storms never blow." It was to inspire that phenomenon among mankind's nomadic movements: the covered-wagon migration. A century later it was to produce maximum yields of every field and fruit crop native to the Temperate Zone, become the continent's leading berry, dairying, and tree-fruit area, and support a population of three quarters of a million people.

On that sundown in the summer of 1832, as the doctor looked southward over what he was later to describe in his journal as "the most salubrious region it has been my lot to visit," there were but nine families living on the soil of the valley, all ex-Hudson's Bay men. Their log houses, garden plots, and growing wheat were grouped close to the river, along the edges of a beautiful meadow known as French Prairie.

The doctor visited with them that night. All knew him as the great man who governed their destinies as completely as he ruled the Oregon Country. The doctor's view toward them was that of a benevolent and affectionate father toward irresponsible children.

"Well, Pierre, I've never seen finer wheat this early in the year. And your cattle and hogs are fat. You're doing all right, eh?"

"*Oui, m'sieu.* Our little ones will never be hungry or cold. There is only one thing——"

"What is it?"

"We need the priest. The little ones should be baptized."

"I know, Pierre. I've asked Montreal to send out a priest.

I've written the London office. A padre will be along, don't worry."

"That is fine, m'sieu. We have many sins to confess."

"And many blessings to be thankful for," the doctor said. "God has been good to us, *mon vieux*."

The doctor meant it. In spite of his fiery temper and the ruthlessness with which he defended his empire, he was a deeply religious man. The doctor's own wife was an Indian woman, the widow of a former Company associate. Most of his officers had Indian wives, all married by the civil ceremony known as the Company Compact. Social life at the fort was highly decorous. No drunkenness or loose living was tolerated.

When they were on the river again, returning to the fort, the doctor grew confidential with Douglas with respect to the probable future of the valley. Douglas was a handsome, cultured youth of twenty-eight, destined to become one of the great figures in Hudson's Bay history. He was the only one at the fort permitted to speak familiarly to the doctor.

"Never breathe it to a soul, Douglas, but the valley *will* be settled someday. God didn't make such soil to stand idle. Wherever crops can grow like that, there'll be men to raise them."

"Yankees, perhaps?"

"No Yankees! . . . Well, yes, Douglas. Even the Yankees, if they've the heart to cross the continent and battle for it. But not for many years yet, mind! We'll fight them every inch of the way!"

Douglas chuckled. "You're a sheep in wolf's clothing, Doctor. With tears of understanding in your eyes you'll mow the Yankees down?"

"These infernal Yankees!" the doctor muttered. "At least we've cleared the country of them for the moment."

In September of 1834 the Yankees seemed to be coming from all directions. Nathaniel Wyeth had returned, as he had

59

threatened to do, financed for a longer battle. He had sent his ship, the *May Dacre*, around the Horn while he led a party overland. He came by way of South Pass, and easy crossing of the Rockies.

Simultaneously news came from California that other parties of Americans headed by Hall Kelley and Ewing Young were approaching from the south.

Dr. McLoughlin was unworried. He was ready for them. When Wyeth and his party arrived at the landing below the fort the doctor greeted them warmly. Though he was prepared to crush their enterprises without mercy, his hospitality was unbounded. Moreover, he liked Wyeth, who was cultured and capable—and a good loser.

The doctor was immensely pleased when Wyeth, introducing each of his party, came at last to a tall, quiet, rough-hewn man with toil-scarred hands and blue, kindly eyes.

"And this, Dr. McLoughlin, is the Reverend Jason Lee. He and his three assistants joined our party at Independence."

"*Reverend* Lee?" the doctor repeated, his face lighting. "It is a pleasure, sir, to welcome a man of God."

"Thank you, Doctor. And this is my nephew, Reverend Daniel Lee. And Mr. Shepherd. And Mr. Edwards."

"I am delighted, gentlemen! Welcome to the Oregon Country! You intend to bring the Gospel to the Indians, Reverend Lee?"

"To the best of my ability, sir," Jason Lee said humbly. "I hope to start a mission east of the mountains."

"Nonsense, sir! You'll start a mission right here. We have a huge Indian population. This wilderness needs you. . . . But we'll discuss it after supper. Let's go up to the fort." The doctor led the procession up the slope. "How have you been, Wyeth? What d'ye mean coming out here after losing your shirt the first time, Eh, lad?"

"This time I'll leave with the Hudson's Bay's shirt," Wyeth

promised. "At least I'm wagering a substantial investment that I will."

The doctor smiled. "Very well. When you're hungry, call on me."

The doctor treated the Americans, including the missionaries, like distinguished guests. He showed Jason Lee the fort, the farm enterprises, and the shops. Lee was intensely interested in everything. At the doctor's invitation he preached at the fort that night—the first church services conducted by an ordained minister west of the Rockies. He spoke plainly and simply, with a sincerity which reached the hearts of all.

But the doctor had not been called the White-Headed Eagle for nothing. The keenest eyes on the frontier had been studying Jason Lee. Late that night the doctor and Douglas sat alone in the office, discussing their visitors.

"You know, Douglas, perhaps I've a quaint notion about ministers and the like, but it does seem that Mr. Lee——"

"I know," Douglas said. "He lacks a little of the polish one expects of gentlemen of the cloth. He seems goodhearted, though. He has high ideals."

"Of course, of course! I like him as a man. But—well, maybe I'm old-fashioned. I haven't been in civilization for a long time. As a boy I looked up to church people. They were aloof, mysterious, *superior* men. D'you understand me?"

" 'The rank is but the guinea's stamp,' " Douglas quoted lightly. " 'The man's the gowd for a' that.' "

"Yes, yes! Well, see that they get over to the valley. Take care of them. Give them all the supplies they need. I'll be busy taking the measure of this infernal Wyeth and his crew. They'll rue the day they crossed swords with me, Douglas!"

The doctor's campaign was ruinous to the Yankees. He easily dispersed the invaders from the south, headed by Hall Kelley and Ewing Young. Kelley returned East the next spring. Ewing Young became a hermit in the valley, embittered and savage.

61

Wyeth was more stubborn, but each of his attempts at trade failed. By the spring of 1836 he was completely ruined. When word came that a British ship entered the river Wyeth came up to the fort almost jauntily to call on the doctor.

"What can I do for you, sir?" the doctor inquired.

"I've come to you for advice," Wyeth said cheerfully. "First, my fort on the Snake has proved a bad investment. Your competing fort has taken all the business. What should I do with my establishment up there?"

"Abandon it."

Wyeth nodded. "Oddly enough, that had occurred to me. Consider it abandoned. Now, my fort here on the river has lost money. I can't persuade the Indians to trade with me. My capital's gone. What would you suggest?"

"I'll buy out—for a price."

"I was sure you would," Wyeth said, smiling at Douglas. "Name your price—just so it's enough to pay my passage back to Boston on this ship that's just arrived. Some of my men want to stay here. I can't abandon them without your assurance——"

"I'll see that they don't starve."

"Good! That concludes our business. . . . Douglas, have you learned something from this exchange?"

"I have, indeed; you're a good loser, sir."

"Thank you—but what I meant was, have you learned anything from the doctor's strategy?"

"I'm at the feet of the master," Douglas said. "Though I'm reserving judgment on a detail or two."

So the victor and vanquished parted with mutual friendliness. Wyeth cheerfully left the fort and the Oregon Country. He went back to Boston, where a successful business career awaited him.

Douglas's last remark had annoyed the doctor. When they were alone again he referred to it sharply.

"What did you mean, Douglas—that you're still reserving

judgment? Haven't we cleared the river of these infernal Yankees? We're on top of the world, man!"

"So it seems," Douglas said. "But you haven't been over to Champoeg lately."

"You mean those missionaries? Bah! They're teaching the Indians how to cook, and to bathe regularly, and till the ground. Worthy work, and all that—but what of it?"

"They're Americans. They're attracting other Americans. Ewing Young's men, for instance. Wyeth's. That shipwrecked sailor."

"Nonsense! They're outnumbered. Lee's only interested in his mission."

"Perhaps. But isn't there an old saying about apples in a barrel, Doctor? Not that Lee's a bad apple, of course. Far from it. He's a lovable character. But his influence is growing. It's the American influence."

"Listen, Douglas," the doctor said benevolently. "I've a surprise for you. We'll put a sound apple in the barrel—a firm, true British apple. D'ye know who's coming on this ship tomorrow? A Church of England chaplain and his wife! The Reverend Herbert Beaver!"

Douglas was delighted. "No! Church of England, eh? That's wonderful!"

"Now we'll see the difference between Lee's methods and the true dignity of the Church, Douglas! You'll see the Reverend Beaver set up a standard that the people will respect. Lee has influence, does he? You'll see how British influence works, m'lad!"

"Hm-m," Douglas said, stroking his jaw. "Won't he have to be protected from the Indians at first?"

"What d'ye mean?"

"This is fur country. Isn't it risky to have another *Beaver* running at large?"

The doctor glared at him. "Keep a respectful tongue in your head, Douglas!"

"Yes, sir."

The next day the ship docked at the landing below the fort. The doctor and his staff went down with high hopes to welcome the Reverend Herbert Beaver and his wife.

The Reverend Beaver was a plump, smooth-cheeked little man. His wife was gaunt and suspicious. An air of martyred condescension surrounded them both. Their viewpoint was plain: their pious duty had driven them from neat, clean England into the midst of barbarians, savages, and squalor. Douglas disliked them on sight.

The doctor was cheerful, however. He led the procession up to the fort, pointing about him proudly with his gold-headed cane.

"Well, Reverend Beaver, did you ever see better wheat and oats? We'll have better than five thousand bushels this year. And wait till you see our pigs! That's a bonny sight. We'll look at them this afternoon."

"I assure you, Doctor," said Reverend Beaver in high-pitched British accents, "that I haven't the slightest interest in your piggery. . . . Those are the sties yonder, I presume?"

"Well, no," the doctor admitted with a touch of embarrassment. "That's the Indian village."

"Really? Why allow them so close?"

Mrs. Beaver sniffed. "I must say, Doctor! Are they really *human?*"

"They are, Mrs. Beaver. And mighty fine people, when you understand them. I don't allow them inside the gate, of course."

"But I say—there are two Indian women inside the gate! What gaudy creatures! You'll ask them to leave, of course, before inviting us in?"

"I will *not*," the doctor said strongly. "Madam, those 'gaudy creatures' happen to be Mrs. John McLoughlin and Mrs. James Douglas!"

"Really?" Mrs. Beaver gasped.

"Incredible!" the Reverend Beaver whispered.

From that unfortunate beginning the atmosphere at the fort steadily grew more strained. Mrs. Beaver was constantly horrified at her primitive surroundings. The Reverend Beaver had no interest in the Indians. He criticized the way the men at the fort dressed, their table manners, their conversation. He was astounded to learn that *all* the wives of Company officers were women of Indian blood.

The doctor was driven close to apoplexy. Douglas went about his duties with swollen and poker-faced dignity. One night, after two weeks of this, the doctor called a sudden conference of Beaver, Douglas, and himself.

"Reverend," the doctor said bluntly, "let's have a meeting of minds. What good are you to this country?"

The Reverend Beaver stared at him, then turned to Douglas with a raised eyebrow. "Is the man mad, Douglas?"

"Not yet," Douglas returned gravely. "But there's a storm brewing in the mountains."

"Quiet, sir! . . . Well, Reverend? Do you plan to teach the Gospel to the Indians?"

"Your manner verges on impertinence, Doctor," said Beaver. "I'll excuse it because of your many years in this brutalizing environment."

"What?"

"Quite. . . . Yes, I shall give religious counsel to any of the heathen that ask for it. But they must scrub up a bit before I'll talk to them. They're incredibly filthy."

"Hm-m," the doctor said. "Reverend, there are some American missionaries over in the valley. Wouldn't you like to visit them?"

"They call themselves Methodists, don't they?" Beaver shook his head. "No, I don't care to associate with them."

"Just how *do* you justify your existence?"

"Really!" Beaver laughed and stood up, glancing at Douglas. "But no—I mustn't allow myself to be annoyed. My work

65

is here at the fort, Doctor. This is the heart of the country's corruption."

"What? *My* establishment is corrupting the country?"

"Of course. I'm putting it all in my report to London. A copy will go to your superiors."

The doctor choked. "Why, you—you fatheaded——"

"Wait," Douglas interposed. "Reverend Beaver doesn't understand that such a report will have to be read by us before it goes to London."

Beaver shrugged. "Certainly you may read it," he said to Douglas. "I'll have it ready tomorrow. You may have to explain it to the doctor, however. His mentality seems to have definite limits."

"Reverend," the doctor said, fighting for self-control, "I think—perhaps—you'd better go to bed . . ." He exploded suddenly: "Before I kick you upstairs!"

"Sir! Are you aware——"

"Run for the hills, Reverend!" Douglas warned.

Beaver blanched and scuttled away. "I must say! My word! This is incredible!" His astounded outcries faded.

The doctor sat down heavily, his face contorted. Douglas hurried away.

The next day came the incident that shattered the dignity of Fort Vancouver. A crowd had gathered in the square to attend an auction. The doctor saw Beaver there and burst out of his office like a grizzly, waving Beaver's report with one hand and his cane with the other.

"Just a minute, Beaver! . . . Now, sir, what's the meaning of this?"

"I knew you wouldn't understand the report," Beaver said. "What item, particularly, do you find puzzling?"

"That I and my officers are living in sin and depravity!"

"Well? Are you married to these Indian women you consort with?"

"Why—why——" the doctor sputtered. "Certainly we're married! We've all been married under the Company Compact, in the presence of witnesses!"

Beaver smiled pityingly. "But not in the Church, my dear fellow."

"How could we be married in the Church, ye numskull! There wasn't any church! Does that make our marriage any less sacred and proper? This report's an insult to God-fearing men and women, Beaver!"

Beaver turned away contemptuously. "Ask Douglas to explain it. He's a bright lad. . . . No, don't threaten me with that cane, you villain! You wouldn't dare!" Suddenly the air was filled with his terrified screams. "Help! I say—stop it! He's killing me! Douglas—help!"

"Tallyho!" Douglas's distant voice added to the din. "Yoicks! Yoicks! Lay on, Macduff!"

To the delight of the spectators, the doctor not only caned the outraged Beaver thoroughly but pursued him across the square and up the stairs. Then the doctor returned to his desk, seated himself heavily, and sat for a long time with his head in his hands. None dared come near him.

But when the auction got under way the doctor sent a clerk to escort Beaver to the square. There, in the presence of all the people, he humbled himself.

"Reverend Beaver, I take this occasion to apologize publicly for the indignity you suffered at my hands. It was an un-Christian act, and I can only hope you can find it in your Christian heart to forgive me."

"Sir," said Beaver, "you are a depraved and unprincipled savage. Your apology is *not* accepted."

The doctor drew himself up and stilled the indignant crowd with an upraised hand. "You will proceed with the auction, Douglas."

The next day the doctor and Douglas went over to the

valley to visit Lee's mission. The community had grown during the preceding four years. In addition to Lee's mission and the homes of the old Company men, the smoke from several other cabins rose up in distant groves.

The doctor's keen eyes studied Lee's establishment. It was a combined school, dining room, and dormitory. At the end of the inspection he said gently:

"A few questions, Reverend Lee. D'ye mind?"

"Not at all, sir. Don't you think we've done pretty well?"

"You have, indeed. You take Indian children here?"

"Yes, there are eight now, including an orphan from the Umpqua."

"They sleep here? You cook for them?"

"Of course."

"Reverend," the doctor said, "don't you find these young heathen a little—er—filthy?"

Lee laughed. "It's nothing that won't wash off. They learn fast. We're expecting some reinforcements from the East. There'll be some ladies too. They'll pitch in and help."

"I'm sure they will. Yes. . . . Any questions, Douglas?"

"I think not." Douglas chuckled. "It looks like good apples in the barrel, Doctor."

"That reminds me," the doctor told Lee. "Our apple tree over at the fort bore well this year. Come over in the fall and we'll let you have a few seeds."

Out on the Willamette River, as their bateau carried them swiftly toward the fort, Douglas laughed heartily.

"It's just as I thought! You've won the battle, Doctor. You're losing the peace."

"What d'ye mean?"

"There are seventeen Americans back there at French Prairie. They're planting wheat that came from the fort. They're milking cows you furnished. And reinforcements are coming for Lee's mission."

"Let them come, you young upstart! They're not afraid

to work. They don't put on airs. They're kind to the Indians. They love the soil. If I can't keep them out, will I see them starve once they're here? . . . But they'll never starve here, Douglas. Not in this beautiful valley. They'll be here long after the fur trade's gone."

1834 – 1836

Jason Lee's mission, begun by four men, formed the nucleus of the American settlement in the Willamette Valley. The settlement grew slowly as reinforcements for Lee's mission arrived from the East, and wandering trappers and adventurers trickled in across the mountains.

Most of these wanderers stayed, having glimpsed the valley. There was something about the vast but sheltered basin of the Willamette that appealed to men weary of mountain and desert. Life here had an Arcadian ease. Summers were indescribably pleasant. Game and fruit were abundant. Winters were mild. The land was rich and free.

The doctor, watching from the fort, knew in his heart that it would only be a question of time before the settlers crowded out the fur trade. He assumed, however, that it would be at least a generation, perhaps a half century, before the hold of the Hudson's Bay Company would be broken. The Company owned all the cattle in the region. Fort Vancouver was the only place where wheat could be sold and supplies purchased. It seemed like a complete and unassailable monopoly.

Yet one man, singlehanded, defied that iron rule. A stubborn Yankee settler—one of the few implacable enemies the doctor ever made—successfully challenged the mighty Hudson's Bay on its own ground.

VI

EWING YOUNG—THE UNFORGIVING

Ewing Young, a quiet, lean-jawed Southerner, led a party of nine men north from California in the spring of 1834. They arrived at Fort Vancouver penniless and half starved and found the gate of the fort barred against them. The governor of Spanish California had sent private word to the doctor that Ewing Young and his crew were bandits and horse thieves.

That was enough for the doctor. There was no room for such vagabonds in the Oregon Country! He allowed but one of the nine Yankees inside the fort: Hall Kelley, who was near death. He gave Kelley medical care but extended none of the usual courtesies of the fort. The others he warned away.

Kelley presently returned East, embittered and broken. Ewing Young refused to leave the Oregon Country. He and his remaining seven men retired to the Willamette Valley and scattered, each for himself. His men were philosophical about the Company's harshness, but Ewing Young, filled with burning resentment at the doctor, announced that he proposed to battle the Hudson's Bay to the end.

He was like a rock tossed into a peaceful pool. Minor ripples soon reached the fort. One day the Assistant Chief Factor, James Douglas, paused at the doctor's desk.

"I think this detail needs your masterly touch, doctor. A bale of beaver skins has just come in from a corner of the valley called the Chehalem. From a Yankee settler."

"Buy them!" the doctor said impatiently. "We're in the fur business!"

"He wants to buy food," Douglas went on. "He's ordered flour, bacon, and salt."

"Sell it to him! What of it?"

"But his name is—Ewing Young."

"What?" the doctor shouted. "Don't buy hide or hair from him! Sell him nothing! Send the furs back!" He glowered up at Douglas. "Is that bandit still in the country?"

"All of them are. Except Kelley, of course."

"Who's been feeding them? Who's supplied them with clothes and the like? Lee's mission, eh?"

"Lee's fed them, but that's all," Douglas said. "They're living from hand to mouth, except Ewing Young. He's built a cabin on the Chehalem."

The doctor's face swelled. "They've got to be driven out, I tell you! These mountain men are the scum of the earth. Lee can't harbor vermin like that. I'll speak to him about it. Meanwhile, send those infernal furs back to Young! The impudence of him!"

"That's where I need your masterly touch," Douglas said cheerfully. "This is Young's only chance to buy food. He won't take help from the other settlers. I gather he's close to starving."

"Let him starve! It's good enough for him! Why isn't he back in the Rockies?" The doctor turned back to his desk, muttering, "Horse thieves! I've trouble enough with honest Yankees. Rats breed rats. . . . Er—he's actually *starving*, Douglas?"

"So it seems. The Indian who brought the furs says he's in mighty poor flesh."

"Send the furs back! I'll have no truck with him! . . . But send a little flour, Douglas. And salt."

"And bacon?"

"Yes, yes! And some coffee. And sugar. . . . What are you laughing at, ye grinning ape?"

"Nothing. I was just wondering. When you cut Ewing Young's throat, which knife will you use?"

"Which knife?" the doctor repeated. Then he exploded: "So it's more humor, is it? Can we sit here, in the midst of plenty, and see a man starve? Even a blackguard like Young?"

"It's out of the question," Douglas agreed gravely. "But I thought I'd better ask."

"Get out of here, then! I'm a busy man, Douglas!"

"Yes, sir."

Ewing Young was too proud, too tough-fibered, to accept charity from the man he now hated with all the force of his character. He brought the food back, untouched, and demanded to see the doctor. The doctor did not refuse. He feared nobody. But the sentry watched from the gate, his musket ready, and Douglas stood by with a dragoon pistol thrust under his belt when the tall Tennessean strode in, weak from hunger but white with rage, and tossed the bundle of food on the floor.

"There you are, suh," he said, breathing heavily. "I thank you kindly, but I won't touch a *gift* of food from you, Doctor."

The doctor nodded, his blue, fierce eyes fixed upon the Yankee. "Very well, Young. What else?"

"I understand, suh, that you look upon me as a horse thief."

"That's correct. That's the word I received from Monterey. An official notice from the governor of California."

"The governor of California lied, suh. It's a little late for this question, Doctor, but——hasn't it occurred to you that I *might* be an honest man?"

"Naturally. As a matter of fact, Young, you've the look of a man unjustly accused. But until you're cleared of this charge——"

"If necessary, suh, I'll go down to Monterey to prove they lied!"

The doctor nodded approvingly. "I've already written the

75

governor, asking him to investigate with care. It may be just hearsay. If he clears you, I'll publish it at once—here at the fort and over at Lee's mission. In the meantime——"

"In the meantime and at any time, suh, I want nothing from you at all. I don't like the Hudson's Bay Company. I don't like you, Doctor. I will personally do everything in my power——"

Douglas interrupted sternly: "No threats, Young, if you please."

"It's all right, Douglas," the doctor said. "He's declaring himself fair and square. He isn't the man to snipe from behind a bush."

"That is correct, suh. But I will use every weapon that comes to hand. Remember that! . . . And now—good day, gentlemen."

"Hm-m," Douglas said, watching Young stride erectly away. "I gather he's no friend of ours."

"He'll be a thorn in the Company's side, no doubt of that." The doctor sighed. "These infernal Yankees! *Must* they be so stiff-necked?"

Ewing Young began his campaign almost within sight of the fort. On the island called Wapato—known today as Sauvie Island—Nathaniel Wyeth had left some large vats designed for salting salmon. Presently the Indians brought word that Ewing Young and his cronies had taken over these vats, built fires under them, and were brewing strange medicine.

The mystery was soon explained. Ewing Young had hit upon the precise thing designed to annoy the doctor the most —he had built a still and was preparing to brew some Tennessee whisky.

The doctor was instantly aroused. Liquor was used only sparingly at the fort, on state occasions. He allowed no liquor traffic at all with the Indians. He sent Douglas over at once to buy out Ewing Young.

Douglas crossed the river in his canoe that night and soon came abreast of the Yankee campfires. From the sound of it, Ewing Young and his men were already sampling their newly manufactured wares.

Douglas hailed the camp. "Hall-oo-o, there! This is James Douglas from the fort!"

The drinking song broke off abruptly. Ewing Young whispered with satisfaction: "It fetched him, men. Quiet, now. . . . Step up, Mr. Douglas!"

Douglas strode cheerfully into the camp. "Well, well, Young! Distilling a little rum, eh?"

"Down in Tennessee, suh," Young returned, "we call it 'moonshine.' "

"You can't make it here, Young. You know that."

"Yes, we can, suh. We're doing it."

"We'll buy you out."

"No, suh. This manufacturing plant ain't for sale."

"You're sure?" Douglas said sternly. "You're defying the Company?"

"Precisely, suh."

There was nothing further to be said. Douglas shrugged, wished them good night, and returned to his canoe.

Ewing Young lost that round, but not to the Company. The settlers themselves grew alarmed about the still. Jason Lee formed a Temperance Society which was joined by a majority of the settlers, including the French-Canadian Company men.

Lee led a delegation which called on Ewing Young and offered him sixty dollars—an enormous amount to the almost penniless settlement—if he would abandon the still. The offer touched the grim Tennessean's heart when no threats could have moved him.

"No, Reverend Lee," he said simply. "I cain't take the money. Your womenfolks and young ones need it. I bow to public opinion, suh. As of now, this manufacturing enterprise has shut up shop."

"That's fine! We honor you, sir."

"I only started it to pester Dr. McLoughlin," Ewing Young went on. "Now I aim to tell you folks a thing or two about the Hudson's Bay Company. . . . Reverend, what does the doctor pay you for wheat over at the fort? Fifty cents a bushel?"

"That's correct."

"And down in California, at Yerba Buena, the doctor sells the same wheat for a dollar and a half a bushel! Is that treating us right?"

Lee hesitated. The doctor had been very kind to the settlers. "Well—he has to make a profit, of course."

"And keep the settlers from getting ahead! Now let's talk about cows. When you settled in the valley, didn't he promise you all the cows you needed?"

"He's done so. The terms, I must admit——"

"Precisely, suh! You have the milk from the cows, but *all* the calves have to be turned back to the Company. Don't you see, Reverend, that we all could stay here a hundred years and be right where we started? He's got a strangle holt on the country!"

"It does seem a little hard," Lee admitted. "But what can we do? Where can we get cows?"

"Down in California. At three dollars a head. We could drive them up. It'll take a little capital, of course."

"Yes—capital. That's the rub. All the cash hereabouts——"

"I know!" Ewing Young said bitterly. "It's over at Fort Vancouver!"

The idea of breaking the Company's monopoly on cattle seemed hopeless to everyone but Ewing Young. He retired to his cabin on the Chehalem and bided his time. He had the stamina of a wolf, the patience of a gambler who is certain in his heart that Lady Luck will one day stand at his shoulder smilingly.

In the winter of 1836 Lady Luck smiled. Into the river

on the brig *Loriot* came William A. Slacum, an agent of the American government, bearing orders to study conditions along the Columbia. Reports from Lee's mission had begun to circulate through the Eastern states. Letters to friends of the missionaries told of the beauty of the Willamette Valley, its mild climate and rich soil. They had attracted notice in high official places. Americans had equal rights in the Oregon Country under the treaty of 1818. How were these rights being respected?

Ewing Young told Slacum about the cattle situation and explained his dream of driving livestock up from California. Slacum listened and invested five hundred dollars. A few of the settlers added small amounts. Those with no money offered to go along on the expedition and take their pay in cattle. Ewing Young was made head of the venture.

News of the proposed cattle drive soon reached Fort Vancouver, and the settlers expected a blast of defiance from the Hudson's Bay. Instead, the shrewd old doctor sent five hundred dollars as the Company's share.

Douglas was staggered by this gesture.

"I say, Doctor—you'll *help* the settlers bring in cattle? The very thing you don't want?"

"There're three reasons, Douglas," the doctor told him confidentially. "This American agent, Slacum, must be given a good impression of the Company. We co-operate with the settlers."

Douglas smiled. "Co-operate?"

"There's no deceit in it! We *are* co-operating—five hundred dollars' worth! The second reason is that *if* Ewing Young and his crew are crooks, we'll never hear of them again after they reach California. They'll abscond with the gold. And cheap at the price."

"I'm at the feet of the master," Douglas said. "The third reason?"

"*If* they get to California, and *if* they can buy cattle—which

I doubt—and *if* they start back, will they ever make it to the valley? Seven hundred miles—over the mountains, with hostile Indians dogging them every step of the way? It's impossible, Douglas! They'll never make it!"

The brig *Loriot* presently put out of the river, taking Ewing Young and his helpers to California. With them was fifteen hundred dollars in gold to pay for the cattle. Many thoughts followed the small brig that day as she dropped down the broad Columbia. To the settlers the cattle were the literal symbols of freedom. All knew how tremendous were the odds against success. Only a few seasoned horsemen like Jedediah Smith and his party had ever made it north from California. How could cattle hope to survive the mountains and the Indians?

The Hudson's Bay Company was in communication via ship with California. News came that Ewing Young and his men had arrived at Yerba Buena and had left for the south to buy cattle.

The doctor was unimpressed. "They'll never be back, Douglas. They'll keep going south."

But another ship, in midsummer, brought later news. The Yankees had left the bay with six hundred cattle and were moving up the Sacramento.

"And here's a personal letter from the governor," the doctor told Douglas. "It clears Ewing Young of that horse-thief charge. We'll publish it at once. We've done wrong to an honest man, Douglas. . . . But he'll never make it through with the cattle! He'll perish in the mountains!"

Now the news began to come overland. The Indians along the Sacramento sent word to the mountains, and the mountain Indians sent word by runners to the Rogues and the Umpquas. The Umpquas brought word to the upper valley, and fast canoemen paddled furiously toward the fort.

"They're in the mountains, Mr. Douglas! The Yanks made it to the mountains!"

"D'ye hear that, Doctor? Do you still feel lucky?"

"They'll perish in the deep snow! They'll never make it to the Umpqua!"

It was like a horse race—but infinitely more vital to the settlers. It was a race against the mountains and Indians and the deep snows of winter. It was a race against starvation and death. It was a race, literally, for freedom.

They prayed at the mission. Men and women stood on the banks day and night, near the place called Champoeg, waiting for news from the south. It was now late autumn, but the weather was still fair.

Then more canoemen rounded the bend, shouting furiously as they paddled:

"They made it to the Umpqua! Six hundred cows on the Umpqua!"

They made it, finally, to the valley. They were still far from the settlement at Champoeg—one hundred weary miles to the south—but the snows of winter could never touch them now. Hostile Indians were far behind. Ewing Young and his iron men were reeling in the saddle, their last reserves of strength almost spent—but they were on the last lap. They had made it to the valley and were bringing the cattle home.

Over at Fort Vancouver a few days later the doctor said:

"Well, Douglas, they'll reach French Prairie tonight."

"Don't feel badly, sir. Only Ewing Young could have done it. He's a man in a thousand."

"And we'll tell him so, Douglas! We'll go over there and watch them bring the cattle in."

"Do you mean it, sir?"

"Why not? I'll be the first to shake the hand of Ewing Young—if he'll permit me. He's a man, sir! . . . Get out our fast bateau! Get the best men on the paddles! We'll start at once."

Over at the settlement near French Prairie some of the

men had left for the south to be of what help they could to Ewing Young. Those without horses stood on a high point, facing south. All the women and children were there, and the people from the mission, the doctor, and Douglas.

Some of those faces were wet with unashamed tears as a thin, moving line appeared on the far horizon. It broadened and grew thicker, became a sea of tossing horns, with riders to right and left. The sound of it was a low rumble in the quiet of the valley. The bawling of calves could be heard and the shouts of the riders as they turned the stragglers in. They were weary riders, with faces gray as masks of death, but who still rode erect as they came into the homestretch.

Finally the herd was close, spreading out, halting, their heads down; and six hundred cattle—good cattle, *free* cattle —were grazing on the rich grass of French Prairie.

Ewing Young swung down and faced the doctor. The happy crying of the women who welcomed their men home from the most formidable cattle drive in the history of the frontier grew momentarily still as those tall, unsmiling men faced each other—and shook hands with a strong, unhesitating grip.

"Ewing Young," said the doctor strongly, so that all could hear, "I say this gladly: well done, sir!"

"Thank you, Doctor." Ewing Young was too proud to gloat, but his unyielding nature could not pass this moment by without reaffirming its significance. He gestured toward the cattle. "When you come after your share of the herd, suh, you can also take away the Company cows you were kind enough to loan us. We all won't need them any more."

"I can see that," the doctor said, his fierce eyes twinkling. "I'll send for them tomorrow."

Though the iron grip of the Hudson's Bay was not entirely broken, the coming of Ewing Young's cattle marked the definite turn of the tide. They were not the finest cattle—they were, in fact, a nondescript beef strain known as Mexican longhorns—but to the settlers in the valley they were the first symbol of independence.

The longhorns of 1837 were far removed from today's magnificent dairy cattle in the Willamette Valley. Some of the nation's finest herds now graze in the hills and meadows not far from Champoeg. The valley today holds, or has held, all world's records in the Jersey breed in milk and butterfat production. The average income to valley dairymen, per cow, is almost a third higher than the average for the nation. The area lying within a hundred-mile radius of Champoeg, in short, is today classed as one of the most nearly perfect dairy regions of the continent.

Ewing Young's grave lies today in the sunlit valley of the Chehalem, not far from Champoeg. No impressive headstone guards the spot, but the historic record marks it as the resting place of an empire builder. The soft-spoken but flint-like Tennessean was the first to breach the walls of that mighty citadel, the Hudson's Bay. Where he led, others followed.

1836 – 1840

By 1840 there were 106 Americans living at or near Lee's mission in the Willamette Valley. About one third of these were men who baffled and bewildered Dr. McLoughlin. This was not a surprising fact, schooled as the doctor was in human nature. The frontiers of the world had never seen a hardier breed.

They were "mountain men": reckless, jovial, fiercely patriotic. They didn't seem to know about rules. When the doctor told them what to do they thought it over—and did as they pleased. When he threatened them they laughed. When he shut off their supplies they lived off the country like cheerful wolves. They liked the valley and had decided to stay.

Eight of them, banding together, decided to carry on where Ewing Young had left off. The valley still needed cattle, horses, and sheep. They had no capital. The nearest livestock was in Spanish California. How get to California with no money for passage on British ships? How acquire capital to buy livestock?

They were resolute men, with strong bodies and skillful hands. They found a way. It entailed the most remarkable feat of construction ever performed on the frontier. It finished what Ewing Young had begun: it broke the Hudson's Bay livestock monopoly forever.

VII

THE STAR OF OREGON

JOSEPH GALE, mountain man, came up from California with Ewing Young in 1834 and settled on the west side of the Tualatin Plains—or "Tuality," as it was then called—near the beautiful stream known today as Gales Creek.

Joe Gale was a broad, powerfully built man with good-natured, heavy-jawed features. A solid man. He had the reputation of never starting a task that he failed to carry through. He had helped Ewing Young bring the cattle north in 1837. He was a tower of strength among the settlers of West Tuality.

At near noon of a summer day in 1840, Joe Gale paused in his labors near his cabin and leaned on his ax, watching two visitors approach from the east on foot. He recognized both. One was Ralph Kilbourne, a tall youth of slow and deliberate manner. The other was Henry Wood, a cheerful, reckless lad, always full of big ideas.

Henry was in the lead.

"Howdy, Mr. Gale!" he greeted. "How you making out?"

"Hello, Henry. Well, Ralph!" Joe Gale examined the perspiring youths, his eyes twinkling a little. "You lads look a little peaked. When did you eat last?"

"We cain't remember that far back, sir."

"I thought so. Well, let's get over to the cabin. Can you make it that far?"

"Wait," Ralph Kilbourne said. "Better tell him first, Henry."

Joe Gale looked inquiringly at Henry.

"You rasslin' with another big idea, son?"

"This isn't just a fool idea, Mr. Gale," Henry said earnestly. "Seven of us are in on it. You make it eight—and nothing can stop us! . . . We're going to build a ship."

There was a pause, then Joe Gale said: "I must be getting kind of deef, Henry. It sounded like you said, 'We're going to build a ship.'"

"That's right."

"What kind of ship? With sails on it and everything?"

"Don't you laugh at us, Mr. Gale," Henry pleaded. "This is the idea. We'll build it back there on the river. Felix Hathaway will help us. He worked in a shipyard in Boston once. Then we'll sail it to California, and sell it, and buy cattle and horses and sheep—and drive them back!"

"Hm-m," Joe Gale said. "Ralph, what kind of meat you lads been eating?"

"I know it sounds crazy," Ralph Kilbourne admitted. "But we can do it if you'll join up with us. We got to do *something*, Joe. Otherwise the Hudson's Bay's got us licked. Show him the plans, Henry."

"Plans, eh?"

"Yes, *sir!*" Henry said with pride. "Felix Hathaway drew them. Here they are."

They withdrew to the shade and unrolled the plans. Gale had spent some time at sea in his adventurous youth, and the design of the ship at once attracted his interest.

"Well, sir, that's a right nice little sloop! . . . Let's see— fifty-four feet overall. Maybe forty tons. Clinker built. Fore and aft rig . . . Hm-m. Looks like Hathaway knows what he's doing, at that."

"You'll be the captain, Mr. Gale!" In imagination Henry was already on the high seas. "We'll be the crew! We'll take it easy down the coast, doing some trapping and trading on the way——"

"Wait a minute, Henry! You got any notion what it means

to hew out these timbers by hand—and the ribs—and saw those deck planks by hand?"

"It's just *work!*"

"Correct. And what about rigging? And ironwork? And sails?"

"We'll get them from the Hudson's Bay!"

Joe Gale shook his head. "Maybe. Did you ever see the doctor cut his own throat? . . . Well, let's eat. We'll do some more figuring after we've got some strength. We'll need it." He led the way, muttering. "Build a ship, he says! Sure, shoot at the moon!"

"Doggone!" Henry whispered dejectedly. "It looks like Mr. Gale——"

"Sh-h!" Kilbourne warned. "I've seen that look on Joe Gale's face before. When we came to mountains they said 'couldn't' be crossed . . . Boy, we're going to build a ship!"

Ralph Kilbourne was right. Gale knew that to build a ship of even forty tons—hewing each plank and timber from the forest, hammering out each spike by hand, getting the hull afloat, rigging it, sailing it on an ocean which some of the seven had never even seen—was a fantastic idea. Any experienced man should shake his head pityingly at the thought.

But Gale himself was still young—in his middle thirties. He needed cattle and sheep. The settlement needed them. Deep in the rock of his character was a Viking strain. Moreover, he was a mountain man.

When the meal was over and he had named one by one the reasons why the venture couldn't possibly succeed, he leaned back in his chair and shrugged.

"There you have it, boys—it can't be done. Everybody will tell you so. Particularly Dr. McLoughlin." He grinned slowly. "So we'll do 'er!"

"Good!" Henry exulted. "Now they can't stop us!"

"I'm afraid you won't be here when we finish her, Henry."

"Why not?"

"It'll be fun the first year," Gale said, studying him. "The second year it'll begin to pinch. You'll figure you're getting old fast."

"It'll take *two years?*"

Gale nodded. "Some of the boys will stick. Canan. Armstrong. Jake Green . . . Kilbourne, maybe?"

"I'll stick," Kilbourne said quietly.

"So will I!" Henry insisted. "What makes you think——"

"It's all right, Henry. We'll see. Well, boys, it'll take a little while to get squared away here. Meanwhile, get your tools together and pick out a likely spot. I'd say that island in the river where the swans are nesting. Pick out a good straight-grained tree for the keel. Let Hathaway help you pick it out—he knows timber. Start whittling on it. I'll be along later."

News of the enterprise soon spread throughout the valley. Some of the settlers laughed. Some of the Company men tapped their foreheads significantly. There was one puzzling detail—Joe Gale was one of the eight shipbuilders. Whenever Joe Gale put his shoulder to a wagon it usually kept moving.

The work began at Swan Island. The keel of the ship was laid. Her frame was of swamp white oak, her beams and carlings of seasoned fir. They whipsawed her cedar planking from white cedar, the most tedious job of all. It took months; and when the time came to nail the planking to the stout frame, each nail had to be hammered out by hand. This required iron to work with, and they needed iron fittings and rigging.

Gale sent Henry Wood over to Fort Vancouver for these desperately needed supplies. The resulting explosion was a classic. Dr. McLoughlin minced no words.

"You should have come to me in the beginning, Mr. Wood. The Company will sell you nothing!"

Henry was aroused at once. "Why not?"

"You know nothing of the sea. You'll all perish if you try it."

"It's our necks we're risking!"

"And you've no license to sail the seas! I'm the only one who can give you papers—and I'll not take that responsibility, either. You mountain men aren't responsible! You're likely to turn pirates! No, I'll have no part of it."

"You're afraid we might get down to California—and come back with cattle and sheep and horses!" Wood retorted. "D'you think you're going to keep us slaves forever?"

"That's enough!" the doctor said sternly. "None of your impudence, if you please. I'll sell you nothing!"

"Very well! But let me tell you this, Doctor"— Henry shook a threatening finger at the Chief Factor—"there's going to be a change here soon. I've got a rich uncle in the East. You'll be hearing from him!"

"Indeed? *Who* is this uncle?"

"His name is *Uncle Sam.*"

The doctor's face turned purple at this jibe. Later he was amused and told the story often. But he sold them no supplies. After his brush with Ewing Young he knew the caliber of mountain men. This time he proposed to take no chances; they must be crushed at the beginning.

But Joe Gale and his men fought on. They persuaded some of the settlers to buy a few items they desperately needed. It wasn't enough. Winter passed, and spring, and the hull was only partly planked. It was tedious, man-killing, heartbreaking labor.

When their last capital was gone Felix Hathaway demanded his back wages. They couldn't pay, so he gathered his tools and walked off. This was a body blow, but Joe Gale refused to give up.

"We can make it, men. We can finish her. We don't need Hathaway. How about it, Henry?"

"Well—it looks mighty tough, Mr. Gale."

"So we're fair-weather sailors, are we? How about you, Ralph?"

"I'll stick," Ralph Kilbourne said quietly.

"Good! You heard him, men! There's seven of us left!"

A few days later Henry Wood and his pal, George Davis, didn't show up at Swan Island. They came the next day—carrying their rifles, and with knives and powder horns hanging from their belts. Henry began to explain, but Joe Gale cut him off.

"I know, Henry—you're heading for the mountains. It's all right. Every man has to plow his own furrow."

"But are you all staying on? When it's plumb hopeless?" Gale turned on Ralph Kilbourne. "How about it, Ralph?"

"I'll stick."

Joe Gale chuckled. "Well—good luck, Henry."

There were five of them left. It was the summer of 1841. They decided to launch the partly finished hull so they could tow it upriver, nearer the settlement. They did so and christened her the *Star of Oregon*. It was not an impressive ceremony. There was no champagne. No man in the valley —except Joe Gale—believed those bare ribs would ever be planked.

They towed the hull upriver and moored it there. They had neither capital nor credit left. They could do nothing more without equipment from the fort. To top it all, Joseph Gale took sick with fever and ague.

That seemed to be the end. The settlers were sure of it. Gale's faithful four laid down their tools. Even the most stubborn wolves lose heart when the leader of the pack has fallen.

Then in their blackest hour the "rich uncle" of whom Henry Wood had boasted appeared on the river—Commodore Wilkes of the United States Navy, on a tour of inspection of the North Pacific. He was received with great ceremony at Fort Vancouver.

The news soon reached a weather-beaten tent near the

falls of the Willamette, where Joe Gale lay ill and helpless. Racked by fever though he was, new hope came to Gale's indomitable heart. Ralph Kilbourne was with him. Kilbourne had promised to stick to the end, and he was there.

"Go over to the fort, Ralph," Gale directed weakly. "Talk to the commodore. Tell him we got to have rigging."

The idea terrified Kilbourne. "I can't do that, Joe. He's a high-up Navy man. He'd laugh at me!"

"No. Tell him I've been to sea. Tell him how hard we've worked. Tell him what it means to the settlement if we make it. He'll listen. Maybe—he'll understand."

Commodore Wilkes listened and understood. He spoke to Dr. McLoughlin and arranged for all the cordage and iron-work and sea equipment the boatbuilders needed. The doctor couldn't refuse. This was no impoverished mountain man making a request; it was the United States Government.

So Joe Gale sent his men hurrying to the fort for these supplies before "Uncle Sam" left the river. . . .

Now the long, weary tide had turned. Gale needed no better tonic than this: they had rigging; they had gear. His health and strength soon returned. By June of 1842 it was no mere hull moored on the bank of the Willamette. The deck went on, the masts went up, the new shrouds were made fast. By August the *Star of Oregon* was a ship, fully rigged—and what a picture she made!

Long years afterward, lovingly, Joseph Gale described her in a letter to an old friend as follows:

She was 53 feet, 6 inches over all, with ten feet and 9 inches of beam at her widest part. . . . She was clinker built and was of the Baltimore clipper model. She was planked with clear cedar planks. Her spars were made of straight fir sticks and consisted of foremast, top foremast, mainmast, and top mainmast, bowsprit, and flying jib-boom. Thus equipped and painted black, with a small white ribbon running from stem to stern, she was one of the handsomest little crafts that ever sat upon the water.

Yes, she was a good little ship. When all her stores were aboard and she was ready to sail, she drew just four feet and six inches of water and was graceful as a swan. Most of the settlers were there to see her start for California. Even those who had scoffed were touched with awe and pride as they looked out at the neat little ship, with her new sails and rigging and her spotless decks.

Her crew were the faithful four who had never lost faith in Joseph Gale: Armstrong, Canan, Jake Green, and Ralph Kilbourne. Kilbourne—having stuck to the end, as he had promised—stood proudly at the wheel. Beside the wheel, armed with ship's papers issued by Commodore Wilkes, was *Captain* Joseph Gale.

"I knew you'd do it, Joe!" an old settler cackled from the dock. "I knew it all the while! But she's a mighty big ocean, boys! Mighty big! You'll never make it to Californy!"

Joe Gale grinned. "Will you eat the biggest cow we fetch back?"

"Sure will! Hide and hair included!"

"It's a bet, old-timer! . . . All right—cast off! Fend her away, there—keep her clear! . . . All hands on the mains'l! *Haul away—haul away!*"

They dropped down to the mouth of the Willamette and found a stiff wind blowing up the broad Columbia. Here Joe Gale made a jovial flourish he had dreamed about for months. He took over the wheel and spun it hard alee. Up the river they went with the wind, past Fort Vancouver, then came about and swung close inshore.

Most of the fort's population was there, watching this strange and beautiful little sloop knifing gracefully by; and as it drew opposite the landing a flag rose up to the mast-head and floated jauntily and proudly there. It was the Stars and Stripes.

Other American flags had come and gone on the Columbia. This one was symbolic, and those at the fort knew it. It flew from the masthead of the first ship built by American hands out of timber grown on the rich soil of the land now known as Oregon. This ship was free. The men who stood on its tilting deck and the flag that waved above them were free. The Columbia was free.

They knew it at the fort—and bowed to it gracefully. Though Dr. McLoughlin was absent that day, it was James Douglas himself who led the cheering as the *Star of Oregon* —her lee rail awash, her canvas booming, and her new spars glinting in the sun—went footing westward to the sea.

It is scarcely necessary to add, as a historical footnote, that the venture was a success. In California, Joe Gale not only traded the *Star of Oregon* for 350 cattle; he persuaded 42 Americans in California to move their families and livestock north to the valley. Thus the caravan which successfully followed the trail Ewing Young had blazed included 1,250 head of cattle, 600 horses and mules, and 3,000 sheep, which left the valley forever independent of the Hudson's Bay Company.

In the spring of 1843 the rule of the Hudson's Bay Company was still unquestioned north of the Columbia River, but in the south, in the vast Willamette Valley, the American settlers were clamoring for some sort of self-government under the American flag. "Company men" in the valley, outnumbering the Americans, were opposed to any rule other than that of the Hudson's Bay.

The issue was decided in a historic meeting held on the banks of the Willamette in May of 1843. By curious chance —or destiny—the meeting place was at Champoeg, where Dr. McLoughlin had permitted Louis la Bonte to take up land in 1830. The doctor had assumed that at least a generation would pass before land settlers became a threat to the Company. Actually it was just thirteen years.

The major incidents of the thirteen years had prepared the way for the Champoeg meeting. Men of the vision and caliber of Jedediah Smith, Ewing Young, and Joseph Gale made that climactic moment possible. Yet when the critical instant came at Champoeg it was no recognized leader in the valley but a jovial and irresponsible mountain man, Joseph L. Meek, whose voice led those who wavered to their epoch-making decision.

VIII

JOE MEEK—PATRIOT

JOE MEEK—mountain man, Indian fighter, teller of exceedingly tall tales—was a cheerful adventurer with no apparent aim in life other than the satisfaction of his own hearty appetites. He was always hungry, always thirsty. No wolf could smell food farther than Joe Meek. No ear was more keen to detect the sounds of a drinking song in the distance. In any camp and any company his voice led all the rest.

He was tall and muscular, with black, knowing, ever-twinkling eyes. His exploits would fill a large volume: the Indians he slaughtered, the grizzly bears he wrestled barehanded, the icy rivers he swam. For most of these adventures, unfortunately, the sole witness was Joe Meek. Nevertheless, real or imaginary, his stories brought cheer to many a lonely rendezvous in the Rockies and on countless occasions earned Meek a hearty meal, smoking tobacco, and the right to uptilt the camp demijohn.

His known trail emerged from oblivion near Fort Hall in the summer of 1840. Meek was plodding dejectedly toward the fort, his long rifle sloping, trailed by a pack horse which carried all his worldly goods, including his Nez Percé squaw and their black-eyed, stolid baby.

Joe's mood changed with each breeze, and at the moment he was vastly dejected. Though only twenty-nine years of age, he was already a veteran of eleven years in the Rockies. The fur trade seemed to be over. His cronies had scattered.

He felt like Rip Van Winkle. Word had come to him that an old trail mate, Robert Newell, wanted to see him at Fort Hall; and Joe had walked 280 miles to keep the appointment.

He dropped his halter rope outside the fort, which was a sign to his squaw to dismount and make camp, and strode among the near-by tents, looking for Newell. Presently Newell hailed him, and Joe's melancholy dropped from him like an outworn garment.

"Howdy, Newell! What you got roasting there?" Meek's voice startled horses in picket lines a half mile distant.

"Antelope. I knew you'd hit here hungry, Joe."

"*Hungry?* I've chawed the bark off all the jack pines this side of Green River! . . . *Mister* Newell—ain't you going to offer me a drink? Where have you got that demijohn hid?"

"Where you can't find it," Newell returned. "We've got business to discuss. Sit down, now. We'll eat first."

"We shore will! But wait till I take a hunk of meat over to my squaw. She figures she's got to eat at least once a week—I dunno why. Be back in a second."

Ravenous as he was—and he was close to starving—Joe first took food over to his wife and baby. Then he came back and gorged himself on Newell's antelope. Both swore later that he polished off a neat ten pounds.

The world was now good to look upon. Having filled his pipe—with Newell's tobacco—Joe looked about him with kindling interest.

"This your outfit, Newell? What the Sam Hill—*wagons?*"

Newell nodded, his lean, sunburned face grave. Though he was a man of some educational background, he had acquired the easygoing mannerisms of the traders.

"That's what I aimed to talk about, Joe. I've took over these wagons. That missionary, Whitman, left 'em here in '37. . . . Now look, the fur trade's plumb ruined. That's agreed, ain't it?"

100

"It shore is." Joe stretched himself prone with a sigh. "Man! I've et so much my ankles hurt! Newell, d'ye know that baby of mine's started talking already? This morning at sunup, right out of a clear sky——"

"Never mind! Listen. . . . Joe, I'm going to take those wagons and drive 'em down to the Willamette Valley. I'm going to get me a farm and settle down."

"Yeah?" Joe said, yawning. "When they finally crack, it's pitiful, ain't it? Some think they're Napoleon. Others howl like a wolf. Newell, he takes to farming."

"And you're going with me, Joe. I want you to drive one of the wagons. When we get there, you can take up a farm too."

"Me?" Joe laughed heartily. "Joe Meek swinging a grub hoe? Milking cows? Setting rattraps under the corncrib? The excitement would kill me."

"But you'll eat regular. You'll have a roof over your head. You got to think of the future, Joe."

"That's what I'm thinking about," Joe asserted. "Where's that demijohn?"

"Of course," Newell went on craftily, "there's bound to be trouble with the Hudson's Bay. I understand they're trying to run the settlers out of the valley. . . . Maybe you're right, Joe. I can't ask you to get into a free-for-all like that."

Joe Meek looked at him, scowling. "The Hudson's Bay's bullying the settlers? First they clean the country out of fur and then start picking on helpless, simple-minded farmers?"

"That's right. They wouldn't let *you* stay there. They'd run you out in a hurry."

"Run *Joe Meek* out of the valley? Why, doggone 'em! When do we start?"

Newell chuckled. "You'll go along, then?"

"They can't keep me out of the valley! Not Joe Meek!

Who do they think they are? . . . But not in the heat of the day, Newell. Don't rush me. Where's that demijohn?"

They left the fort in the cool of the evening. Joe Meek drove the first wagon. A wanderer named Craig drove the second. Newell, the owner, rode in the lead. As they got under way five other mountain men joined them. It didn't matter which direction they went. It might as well be west.

This casual, carefree, impoverished crew blazed the first wagon trail west of the Snake. Though he received no credit until years later, the first wheeled vehicle to reach The Dalles from Fort Hall was driven by Joseph L. Meek.

They left the wagons at The Dalles and descended by boat through the Columbia's massive gorge. It was now early winter. The five mountain men scattered to various parts of the valley. Newell went to Oregon City, a village by the falls of the Willamette, and got a job building a house for the mission people. Joe Meek drifted over the Tualatin Valley and pitched his tent under a tree.

Joe was soon greatly depressed. It rained and rained. The trees dripped. When his food ran out he went hunting but found that the game had taken to the hills. He came back wet and melancholy, with his moccasins full of mud. The near-by settlers had little food to spare. Their only surplus was wheat.

Finally, in desperation, Meek saddled his horse and hunted up Newell at Oregon City.

"This country's got me, Newell. It rains too much. I've been living like a muskrat."

"It'll be better in the spring."

"I'll never hold out till spring! Newell, I thought I'd seen everything in the way of victuals. I've et dog meat. I've et snakes. Over in the Black Hills, once, I et a mess of ants! But d'ye know what me and my family's been gorging on for the past ten days? *Boiled wheat!* I just can't look boiled wheat in the face any more, Newell. What am I going to do?"

"I hate to tell you, Joe. It's going to hurt. . . . You'll have to get a job."

"A job?" Meek was staggered. "You mean—*work?*"

"That's right. For instance, I'm building this house for the mission people. I could use you on the heavy work."

"Heavy work?" Joe considered this and shook his head. "No, sir—I ain't going to work for the mission people. They look down their noses at me."

"Well, then, you could go over and work for the Hudson's Bay."

"For that bloated monopoly? And British, at that? *Mister* Newell!"

Newell sighed. "I'll tell you what, Joe—I've got some food over at the cabin. I'll split it with you. Us mountain men got to stick together."

"Good! What kind of fodder is it?"

"Wheat. . . . And I'll tell you how to cook it. You bring it slowly to a boil, then add a pinch of salt——"

But Meek hurried away. He went over to Fort Vancouver, but not to work. By hanging around the kitchen at the fort and telling mighty tales about Kit Carson, Sublette, and other heroes of the Rockies—always including that fearless trail blazer, Joe Meek—he lived well that winter. There were always some extra odds and ends of food to take over to the squaw and little one.

By spring he was a legend in the valley. Everybody knew Joe Meek. He was tremendously popular. Dr. McLoughlin couldn't understand why hard-working settlers should be so delighted with each new story describing Joe Meek's latest device to *avoid* hard work. . . . But there was something about Joe Meek. It was hard to lay a finger on it, but it was there. He was a ray of sunshine in a lonely land.

He could smell excitement brewing from afar and hurried to be in the thick of it. If a ship came in he boarded it down-river and helped the crew celebrate their safe arrival. Then he went ashore and helped the fort celebrate the ship's arrival. Wherever there was free food, or the head of a cask was broken in, or the voices of men were raised in argument or song, Joe Meek was there.

The political pot boiled that summer. The American settlers sent memorials to Congress. Ewing Young died, leaving no heirs, and his estate had to be administered. This caused prolonged debate. How administer an estate without a probate court? How set up a court without some form of civil government—*and under whose flag?*

Joe Meek loved this mounting uproar. What pleased him most of all was that the women of the settlement usually set out victuals after each meeting. Good victuals. . . . Roasting ears. Beans. Fine home-cured bacon. Sometimes even—doughnuts!

The meetings soon fell into a familiar pattern. After long debate a short-tempered settler would shout:

"Mr. Chairman, why wait for Congress? I move that you appoint a committee to study out how to set up our own government! We're Americans! We can do it! What are we waiting for?"

A quiet but watchful spokesman for the Hudson's Bay would intervene:

"Mr. Chairman!"

"Father Blanchette."

"I suggest that we postpone action. The Hudson's Bay Company is the civil authority of this region. . . . Incidentally, Mr. Chairman, I speak for the majority of the residents of this valley."

This last—reaffirming the preponderance of Company men —would enrage the Americans. Then a jovial voice would come from the edge of the crowd:

"*Mister* Chairman!"

"*Mister* Meek!"

"I see the ladies have the doughnuts and cider ready. What are we waiting for? I move we adjourn!"

"The meeting is adjourned."

In the spring of 1842 Joe Meek overcame his repugnance for manual labor long enough to plant thirty acres of wheat. It was a depressing experience, and he soon hurried off to other enterprises. Deeper political currents were swirling in the valley. The tension between the settlers and Hudson's Bay was growing.

Joe Meek attended the "wolf" meetings of February and March of 1843, when a committee was finally appointed to study and propose some form of civil government. Their report was to be presented at a "big" meeting scheduled for May 2 at Champoeg.

When that historic meeting was called to order Joe Meek was there. He knew all the American settlers by their first names. He knew all the French Canadians, the Company men. Only men could vote, and almost every able-bodied man in the valley—102 in all—was there.

Joe Meek circulated among them, slapping backs, guffawing loudly, keeping an eye on the tables under the trees, where the ladies were getting the food ready. Presently he came upon two French Canadians, Matthieu and Lucier, whispering together.

"Well, Matthieu! And Lucier! How are you two *loups-garous!* Be sure to vote right, Lucier. *For* the report. We got to have a government!"

Lucier was doubtful. "We are talking about that, Matthieu and I. With a government there is always taxes."

"Taxes?" Meek snapped his fingers. "Ho! I've been an American thirty-three years, my friend. I never paid four bits' taxes in my life!"

Matthieu whispered, "You see, Lucier?"

The motion was made and seconded. The question was the adoption of the committee's report, which called for a provisional government under the American flag until such time as the United States formally took over.

Prolonged debate broke out. The American settlers were for the report. The Company men were against it. Dr. McLoughlin had allowed no employee from the fort to attend the meeting, but Company settlers had their instructions.

Joe Meek listened with mounting impatience. Why all this talk? Why not count noses and get it over with? Finally came the moment that had been inevitable since Captain Robert Gray of Boston had crossed the bar of the Columbia fifty-one years before.

"Question! Question!"

"Gentlemen, the question has been called for. All those in favor of adopting the report of the committee say 'aye.'"

"Aye!" shouted a thunder of voices.

"Contrary?"

An equally impressive roar followed: "No!"

"Gentlemen, the vote is close. We must have a showing of hands." There was a pause, then: "It appears that the motion is lost."

At once there were challenging shouts: "Divide! Divide!"

This meant that each man would be counted, and at that instant Joe Meek stepped jovially from the shadows to meet his destiny. All his thirty-three years—carefree, sometimes misspent years—had prepared him for it. The voice that could attract attention in any gathering, that had roared above many a carousal in the mountains, in many a drinking song, in many a battle with the painted Sioux, now raised Joe Meek to his niche in history.

"Who's for a divide?" he bellowed. "All those for the report *follow me!*"

They followed Joe Meek across the line—all of the American settlers, all those who had previously wavered. All but two. Two French Canadians stood in the middle, undecided: Matthieu and Lucier.

The crowd grew still as realization came. There were fifty men on each side of the line. These two who whispered together would cast the deciding votes.

"Come, Lucier—we must vote with the Americans, yes? If we do not, and this becomes an American country—what then?"

"But the taxes! I am afraid of American taxes! They will eat us up!"

"No, no—they are not bad taxes. Remember M'sieu Meek? All his life he has paid no taxes at all!"

"But has he taken up land?"

"*Oui—oui!* And he has planted wheat. I have seen it."

So they joined the Americans, and the report was adopted: 52 votes to 50.*

Though the men of Champoeg didn't know it, this was a turning point in the path of empire. It was the birth of Oregon.

The French Canadians, led by Father Blanchette, immediately withdrew from the meeting. The Americans went on with the organization. They elected a supreme judge with probate powers, a clerk of the court, four magistrates, a treasurer—and a high sheriff, Joseph L. Meek.

This last honor was Joe Meek's personal and incredible pinnacle of triumph. He cared little for his problematical niche in posterity's hall of fame. He lived in the present; and to be the high sheriff—itself a mouth-filling title—with the attendant responsibility of tracking down criminals, preserving law and order, supervising hangings, and other de-

---

*This is the account given of the controversial Champoeg incident many years later by the then venerable Stephen X. Matthieu. Joe Meek's personal accounts gave color but not authenticity to the record. The notes of the recording secretary, W. H. Gray, have been challenged due to Gray's known bias against the Hudson's Bay Company.

lightful and spectacular chores, *and be paid for it!* Who could ask more? Not Joe Meek!

Thus, on the banks of the Willamette, May 2, 1843, twilight deepened over a crowd of American settlers—neighbors—forming a line beside tables where good food waited. At the head of the line, and not by inscrutable chance, was Joseph L. Meek, High Sheriff of the Territory of Oregon.

This was no ordinary twilight. It marked the fading of a cycle which had begun when Dr. McLoughlin's greatness of heart had permitted the first settler to build his cabin in the rich and beautiful valley of the Willamette, near the place called Champoeg.

1843 – SUMMER

Though the establishment of the Oregon Provisional Government at Champoeg in May of 1843 was a colorful event of that historic year, it was far from being the most impressive.

At the very moment that the enthusiastic settlers were shouting at Champoeg, close to one thousand men, women, and children were converging on Independence, on the south bank of the Missouri. They came in hundreds of covered wagons, accompanied by their livestock and all their worldly goods, ready to embark on the two-thousand-mile trip to Oregon.

Whence came these emigrants, and why? What urge caused them to challenge the trackless plains which lay to the west? What did they hope to find—what did they actually find—at the end of that long and formidable trail?

The answers to those questions comprise the story of one of the most remarkable nomadic movements in the recorded history of man—the "Great Migration of '43."

IX

THE GREAT MIGRATION

THE word "depression" is of recent origin. They called it "hard times" a century ago; and in 1842, in Missouri, Arkansas, Illinois, and western Kentucky, hard times were knocking at the door.

Wheat brought fifteen cents a bushel or less. Corn couldn't be given away. Waiting passengers could smell river boats approaching on the Missouri and Mississippi: they were burning bacon for fuel. Jess Applegate sold a *steamboat load* of bacon that year for one hundred dollars. Men worked on farms for fifty cents a day—not in cash, but in orders for goods on merchants who were themselves bankrupt.

All this was intolerable to farmers along the Missouri, the Mississippi, and the Ohio. They were already pioneers. They were true frontiersmen: used to hardship, completely self-reliant. When the outlook seemed hopeless their instinctive reaction was: move farther west!

All knew about a land far to the west—across the plains, across the continent. Jedediah Smith had written about it. Hall Kelley had preached its promise. Descriptive letters from Lee's mission had been published far and wide. It was called the Oregon Country.

A typical frontier family in Clay County, Missouri, discussed the outlook in May of 1843.

"Out in Oregon I can get a square mile of land," the father boasted. "And a quarter section each for you all. It never gets cold out there. You lads will be healthy. It's close to the ocean, and we can sell all we raise to the Sandwich Islands, and down in Californy, and out in China."

The mother was doubtful. "But it's so *far* away!"

"There'll soon be schools, stores—everything we got here! Everybody along the river's going. It's new country! Tell you what, Maw. You stay here with the young ones. Jim and Pete and I'll get along to Oregon, get located, and then send for you."

"I should say not! Who'd get the victuals for you all and keep your clothes mended? Who'd see that the boys took their baths regular, like Christians? . . . Paw, you're laughing at me!"

"So this outfit will stick together, hey? All right, Jim, you take the buggy horses over to Independence tomorrow. I've traded for a new wagon. Fetch it back fast. Maw, you make up a list of things you aim to take along. Not everything you want to take, mind, but what you *got* to take. It's a long haul."

Multiply this family by a hundred others. Multiply their livestock until their herds include six thousand cattle, horses, and sheep. Give them leaders like Peter Burnett, the Applegates, William Martin, and James Nesmith. Make the rank and file the cream of the border breed. Give them good women and healthy children, good oxen, stout wagons. Picture them assembled on the south bank of the Missouri—a great crescent extending five miles from north to south, the new canvas gleaming whitely in the sun, the campfires twinkling by night in a long, jeweled line joining horizon to horizon.

That enormous cavalcade was what history calls the "Great Migration of '43."

They were not, as many imaginative writings have suggested, a grim and martyred company—sad-eyed, piously offering themselves on the altar of freedom. Their manner of conducting their first business after leaving Independence was proof of their "folksy" caliber.

They halted their long column at the Kansas River to select leaders for the train. There were no formal speeches. Grinning and embarrassed men of local prominence were forced to mount a wagon bed so the assembled multitude could see them and hear their halting words. There was no secret ballot. Like schoolboys playing follow-the-leader, they formed long serpentines behind their respective candidates.

The noise of it rolled across the plains. The longest column would be the winner, and each shouted loudly for more recruits as they circled and weaved.

"Applegate! This way for Jess Applegate! Come on, Illinois!"

"This-a-way for *Kaintucky!* Join up, Arkansas! Join up with Kaintucky!"

"Come on, you Liberty men. *Burnett!* Burnett and old Missouri!"

Peter Burnett was the winner. James Nesmith was appointed orderly sergeant. The huge company was quickly organized. Camp rules were adopted. Everything was harmonious and cheerful as the long column got under way, Oregon-bound. Two thousand miles of wilderness lay ahead, and what of it? A unit of America was moving here—neighbors, brothers all, embarked on a mighty adventure. . . .

This brotherly love lasted just nine days. Never in the nation's history have one thousand Americans been of one mind on any subject. To do so would be contrary to the ways of democracy. There were heated charges of despotism and favoritism. Kentucky claimed that Missouri was "hogging" the best camp site each night. They argued about who would be first in line, who should hunt buffalo, who should herd the despised "cow column."

So they held a vast indignation meeting. Peter Burnett resigned and was replaced by William Martin. The jovial Nesmith stayed on as orderly sergeant. They split the company into separate columns. Those who were traveling light, with no livestock, took the lead. Jesse Applegate took command of the plodding "cow column" which brought up the rear.

Then, more efficiently organized, the "long haul" began. By the time they reached the long sweep of the Platte it was a seasoned army on the march. The unbroken prairie was before them. Behind lay a road deeply marked, a long gash out across the plains. It is still there today, at the Continental Divide—a scar worn deep by the winds and floods of the intervening century. Later trains were harassed by Indians, but this mighty column crawled on in safety, the objects of wonder and awe. The marauding Sioux had not yet recognized, in these creeping wagons, the symbols of their own destruction.

There were tragedy and comedy along the line of march. There were lovers' quarrels. By night, within the circle of wagons, while the campfires flickered and the guards held lonely vigil in the outer darkness, there were singing and dancing—the old dances and songs of Missouri and Arkansas.

There were births along the way. A wagon would pull out of line. A rider would dash ahead for Dr. Whitman, the physician-missionary. Soon the doctor would thunder along the column, his coattails flying. Later, at the "nooning" or in night camp, the wagon would overhaul the column. The doctor would be cheerful, the father haggard but smiling.

"What luck, Jim?" someone would shout. "A boy?"

"Nope. A gal."

"You'll never get a harvest crew at that rate!"

"Maybe not—but she's worth another quarter of free land out in Oregon!"

There was a death on the Platte and another east of Laramie. The whole column halted on each occasion so that friends from the rear or from up forward could take part in the final rites. Later trains rolled their wagons over the graves to hide the spot from prowling Indians. These were buried beside the trail with a simple cross marking the final "night camp."

There was something about the death east of Laramie that touched the hearts of all. It came in the night to a boy of ten, a frail lad. His parents hadn't realized how frail he was. He had been out with the cow column each day. He had been dead tired each night. They tried to make him rest in the wagon all day, but he was too proud. The other boys were up and around!

One morning he didn't get up, and the second morning, when it was time to eat, they couldn't waken him.

There was no dancing that night. The memory of the narrow grave, with its plain wooden cross, was too close in the minds of all. The little trail blazer, the little corporal of the cow column, was no longer in camp. He was alone on the plains, and it was a black night back there—and a big and lonely one—for a boy of ten.

The parents stayed in their darkened wagon, with the endflaps drawn. Nothing could be done for them. Not even the sincere words of Dr. Whitman could soothe their heartache or their tears. But all joined in the singing as the campfires died. It was a song of faith, of hope.

> Abide with me: fast falls the even-tide;
> The darkness deepens: Lord, with me abide:
> When other helpers fail, and comforts flee,
> Help of the helpless, O abide with me!

In the morning the train rolled on. The wheels must be kept rolling. . . . They were rickety wheels now—in late summer—as they crawled slowly up from the Sweetwater. The canvas of the wagons was faded. The oxen were footsore. Autumn was close, and they were still far from Fort Hall; and beyond Fort Hall, for seven hundred unknown miles, even Whitman had never taken a wagon.

Those were grim days which called for all the boasted stamina of frontiersmen. Those were the days when the strong must encourage the weak; when men like Nesmith, Burnett, and the Applegates must ride the length of the column—lending a hand here, shouting encouragement yonder. The wheels must be kept moving. A breath of frost in the air was urging: Roll on! Roll on!

And those were the nights when the song of the trail— "Oh! Susanna"—rolled out as defiantly as ever. The young and strong men of the column sang it, and it was a tonic to spirits beaten and depressed. It was a challenge to the mountains and deserts. When the going was hardest, in the shadow of defeat, it was a salute to victory.

Down at Fort Vancouver, in early October, Dr. McLoughlin heard the unbelievable news. A great American migration comprised of one thousand men, women, and children—*with wagons*—had actually crossed the plains and reached Fort Hall. . . . It was incredible. James Douglas was in the North that month, and the doctor missed him sorely. McLeod was there, but though McLeod was a good clerk, he was no Douglas.

"They can't bring wagons past Fort Hall, Doctor. It's ridiculous! They'll die like flies in the high desert."

"I don't know," the doctor said heavily. "They'll keep coming. Remember Ewing Young and Joseph Gale. . . . And *what* shall I do with them when they come to the gorge?"

"Do nothing, sir! They can't get through. Let them face winter at The Dalles!"

"Without food or shelter? They'll freeze, McLeod! They'll starve!"

"Let them starve."

"But there's women and children, man!" Then the doctor spoke grimly. "And on the other hand, did *we* invite them? I've my duty to the Company to think of! Aye—and my duty

116

to Britain! This wagon-train business must be stopped at the beginning!"

"Precisely, sir."

The immigrants rested for ten days at Fort Hall, then pushed on. They were told it couldn't be done, that no wagons had ever reached the Columbia. Actually, a small band of immigrants had traversed the intervening deserts the year before, led by Dr. Elijah White from Lee's mission.

It had to be attempted, in any event. Winter was just around the corner. Their food was almost gone. They had to get across the Cascades before snow flew.

They almost won their race against winter. They made it up desolate Burnt River and to the Grande Ronde Valley. Then snow caught them in the Blue Mountains. Here, almost within view of the Columbia, they passed two frightful weeks of struggle. James Nesmith led the strongest men ahead with axes to clear a trail through the whitened timber. The women and boys followed with the wagons and cattle.

Finally they crossed the chill summit and came down into the broad, treeless basin of the Umatilla. Due north, not far now, was the Columbia.

In the minds of all the Columbia River was the goal. Nothing could stop them now! The Oregon Country was just beyond the last mountains, the Cascades. They sang in camp on the Umatilla that night, wind-swept, ragged, and miserable though they were.

They sang too soon. They didn't know that this last 240 miles, which included the passage of the Columbia gorge, contained more privation and danger than anything they had yet encountered. Dr. Whitman, who left them on the Umatilla and struck out for his mission at Waiilatpu, hadn't prepared them for the gorge. Whitman had made but one trip to the lower river, in the comparative safety of a Hudson's Bay bateau.

They learned at The Dalles, one hundred miles short of the

valley, that wagons could go no farther. This was the end of the overland trail. The last lap of their trip must be by boat, but where were there boats for such a company?

Winter storms were now howling through the gorge. The settlers sent up a few boats, and when the first chilled and shivering emigrants emerged from the cleft Dr. McLoughlin learned what the bulk of the miserable but indomitable army was attempting to do at The Dalles.

"They're building *rafts*, McLeod! They'll trust their lives— and their women and children—to such contraptions!"

"And they'll drown like rats."

"Aye," the doctor agreed somberly, "some of them will. And meantime, the strongest of them are trying to drive their cattle through. Say what you will, McLeod, they're men of courage!"

"I trust you're not forgetting your obligations, Doctor."

"D'ye have to remind me of them? . . . But what *are* my obligations, McLeod? I'll help those who call on me, of course. But there'll soon be snow in the gorge. Women and children—on *rafts!* What are you nodding for? You don't even know what I'm talking about, ye cold-blooded——" The doctor shrugged. "Never mind. We'll see."

It was a struggle for survival in the gorge. The scattered settlers in the valley couldn't help such numbers. Lee's mission could do little more than care for the chilled and half-starved emigrants who made it through.

Death stood on the banks at the Cascades. Rafts broke up in the savage water. Those who made it ashore were in a desperate plight without shelter or food. The cattle drivers were below, swimming the weakening herds from bank to bank, almost inching their way downstream.

In late November, with rain and sleet driving before a strong upriver wind, word came to the fort that two hundred emigrants—most of them women and children—were marooned at a point called Cape Horn. They could go no farther. Their rafts could make no headway against the wind. They were too weak to travel by land. Huddled in makeshift shelters through which the rain and sleet blew, they were reduced to the final extremity of the bitter trail: they were eating rawhide.

"I can't stand this, McLeod! Half of them will be dead three days from now."

"D'ye mind if I call a spade a spade, Doctor?"

"I know—I must be firm. In any war it's the weak and innocent that perish. Is that it?"

"That's it. Exactly, sir."

It was a three-day storm. McLeod stayed indoors, close to the cheerful fireplace, busy with his accounts. On the third day there was a lull, though the wind moaned on. The doctor came into the office, for a time stood by the fire. Then he spoke abruptly.

"I need some moral encouragement, McLeod. Step down to the dock with me. We'll look at the river."

The doctor led the way, his face grim. They stood on the dock, leaning against the wind, looking upriver. The sun had broken through the clouds low in the west, but a dark curtain still blotted out the mountains and rested on the gray, tossing current of the Columbia.

"That'll be snow up there in the gorge, McLeod."

"Don't feel badly, sir. You can't help those people."

"I know. It would not only be false to the Company, but I'd be accused of being false to Britain. It would also mean that my own career was finished. Nobody cuts his own throat, eh, McLeod?"

"You did your duty, sir."

"But did you ever see a woman lying in the snow, McLeod, still trying to protect her baby—her *dead* baby—from the storm?"

McLeod shuddered. "You've too much imagination, Doctor."

"Aye—and it doesn't mix with duty. . . . Did you ever hear a child crying for food in the night—the *fourth* night of hunger? *I* have, McLeod."

"Let's get back to the fort."

"Don't weaken, McLeod. It shouldn't be long now."

Faintly against the wind, from the driving mists upstream, came the sound of men's voices singing. The song was "Oh! Susanna." McLeod listened, frowning.

"Doctor, I've just noticed something. Where are our big bateaux? All five of them are gone!"

The doctor smiled. "So you've finally noticed it? They've been gone three days."

"Three days? Since before the storm?"

"Yes, and loaded with food. Good beef. Good bread. . . . Here they come, McLeod! Look upriver, man!"

The leading boat was beginning to emerge from the mist. Women were standing in the bow, shading their eyes against the low sun.

"Our bateaux!" McLeod said incredulously. "Loaded with people!"

"Each bateau holds forty," the doctor agreed. "Five times forty is two hundred. They should all be there. . . . Isn't that a bonny sight?"

It *was* a "bonny" sight—five bateaux in line, their paddles dipping rhythmically, emerging from the mists. They were crowded with women and children. It was snowing in the gorge, but the gorge was behind them now. The width of the whitened continent was behind them.

"But, Doctor, you're bound to hear of this! You'll hear of it from Montreal—aye, and from London! You know Governor Simpson's orders!"

"I know," the doctor said, twirling his gold-headed cane. "But Douglas has come along fast during the past five years. He'll make a good Chief Factor here at the fort."

"You mean—you deliberately sacrificed yourself for these *Americans?*"

"They're *people*, McLeod. . . . You wouldn't understand. Pull yourself together, man! We're the reception committee. Don't you see the sunlight on their faces? Don't you see the people smiling?"

The Great Migration was safe in Oregon. More than thirty thousand emigrants followed them over the same route during the next generation. None measured up to the caliber of the trail blazers of '43. They were a superior breed. Peter Burnett later became the first governor of California. James Nesmith was a United States senator from Oregon. The rank and file of the train left their imprint on the social and political life of a great commonwealth.

THE FORMIDABLE '40S

Until a wagon road was opened across the Cascades Range, the gorge of the Columbia was the greatest single hazard the emigrants faced in the two-thousand-mile length of the Oregon Trail.

The gorge—world-famous now—was created when the prehistoric Columbia, disdaining to turn aside when its waters reached the Cascades, had cut a fifty-mile channel directly through the heart of the towering barrier. At certain points the walls of the gorge were a sheer two thousand feet high, with their footing submerged in the speeding current. Long stretches were floored by rapids, or "cascades," from which the mountains were later named.

Every pioneer journal of the '40s mentions the hardships of those last fifty miles. One of these journals was a diary written by a plain, wholesome, unaffected pioneer woman. She didn't record hearsay or rumor about the Columbia gorge. She set down her own experiences. She was there. From that record we learn something of the character and caliber of the most magnificent of all empire builders—the pioneer wife and mother.

X

ELIZABETH SMITH—PIONEER

CORNELIUS SMITH and his wife were still young—in their early thirties—when they joined a wagon train which pushed west from Missouri over the trail blazed by the Great Migration of '43. Young as they were, the Smiths had a family of seven children, the oldest a boy of sixteen, the youngest a babe in arms.

Cornelius Smith was a quiet man of frail physique but unquestioned courage. His wife was small, neat, and matter-of-fact. In spite of her hardships and duties on the long trail, she found time each day to write a line or two in her diary. Through that record shines the complete honesty and simplicity of the woman.

When they arrived at The Dalles, the eastern entrance to the terrifying Columbia gorge, the train broke up, and it was each man for himself. The Smiths had no food left and no money to hire or buy a boat. Cattle must be driven down the north bank to a point above the rapids, or Cascades, then across to the south bank for the lower and more difficult stretch. Meantime the women, children, household goods, and dismantled wagons must ride down through the gorge on rafts.

Storms of wind and rain were roaring through the gorge. Already the mountaintops on each side of the mighty canyon were white with snow. Elizabeth Smith was as calm and matter-of-fact as though she were sitting in a rocker beside a warm fireplace, sewing.

It is October 29 and very rainy and cold [she writes]. There are a great many emigrants in camp. The men are making rafts, the women cooking and washing, the children crying. . . . Indians are trading potatoes for shirts. They must have a good shirt for a half peck of potatoes!

That last statement is significant. No danger of the trail has been remotely comparable to the gorge through which this tremendous, tossing current rolls. She can see the storms raging there—dimming the enormous cliffs, blackening the sky. She is concerned with details close at hand. Like any good housewife, she is indignant about these grasping Indians. "Just imagine!" (we can almost hear her say.) "A good shirt for a *half peck* of potatoes! The heathen!"

The raft was finally finished. It was made of forty-foot pine logs lashed together. Three other adults joined the Smiths: Adam Polk and his wife, and an easygoing giant named Russell Welch. The three men and two women held a conference that night after the children were in bed.

Adam Polk—a gaunt, kindly man, hollow-eyed from a racking cough—had a suggestion to make.

"A feller over at the mission tells me it'll take three men to handle the raft down below. So how's this for a proposition, Smith? You and me and your oldest boy take the raft through while Welch and your two younger boys drive the cows."

"Sounds good," Smith agreed. "Suits you, Welch?"

"Sure. I don't want the responsibility of the womenfolks and the young ones. That's a mighty big river. We'll see you at the Cascades—if you all make it that far."

"We'll make it," Polk said, coughing. "It ain't but forty miles or so."

"You're getting consumption, Adam Polk!" his wife said, alarmed. "I knew you would! I told you not to wade out in that cold water, working on the raft!"

"Sho! We'll soon be to the valley."

"One thing worries me," Welch said. "Me and the boys will have plenty of grub if we get snowed in. We got the beef with us. But you folks are mighty short. You reckon we'd better kill that red heifer of yours before we start out, Smith?"

"No, sir! We'll need that heifer when we get to the valley. We've got enough victuals for a week, haven't we, 'Lizabeth?"

"Well—I think so," his wife said doubtfully. "It had better not take any longer."

"Longer? If it does, we'll get off and walk. Three days is my guess."

Fortunately none of them could read the future. Not three days but three nightmare weeks lay ahead.

On November 2 the raft shoved off. All their household goods and their dismantled wagons were lashed to it. Surmounting the pile were the two wagon beds with their canvas tops. Smith, his oldest boy, and Polk manned the poles. Welch and the younger boys had already disappeared into the mists with the cattle.

The forty-foot raft was so unwieldy that it required the combined efforts of all to fend away from the rocks. They made only a few miles the first day, then put ashore to wait for the wind to die down. That night was the worst since leaving the Missouri. Elizabeth Smith recorded it calmly.

It is impossible to sleep on the raft, so we clamber up a side hill among the rocks and build a fire to cook and warm ourselves and the children. All night the wind blows and the waves roll beneath.

It was an unusually bad season. Down in the valley it was comparatively calm, but the wind never stopped howling through the gorge. The rain changed to sleet. Each day they ventured out into the tossing current, inched downstream a few miles, then tied up again.

There was no turning back. Once in the gorge, they must battle on. At some points cliffs two thousand feet high rose almost vertically from the river. Somewhere above those cliffs, in the whitened timber, Welch and the two small boys were fighting the mounting drifts.

The provisions on the raft ran out on the seventh day. Adam Polk stayed in bed, desperately ill. Smith and his boy managed the raft, hoping for a lull in the wind. At times the wind overcame the pull of the current and the raft made no progress at all.

That night was bad. With plenty of food they could have battled both cold and weariness. Without food the Cascades were far away. . . . And Mrs. Polk was gripped by another fear—the ultimate tragedy to a woman on the trail.

"He's dying, I tell you! Don't you understand? *My man's dying!*"

"Don't you say that, Mis' Polk. They'll take care of him in the valley."

"He'll never make it! He's fighting for every breath! Oh, I *wish* we'd never left Missouri!"

"Don't you worry, honey. Hush! Maybe the wind will stop blowing."

They had to have food. The younger children wailed with hunger in the night. The next morning Smith decided to forage down-river on foot. He might meet some Indians or settlers. He promised to bring something back.

Mrs. Polk grew hysterical. "Don't let him go! He'll never get back. You'll see! We'll be all alone in this terrible canyon!"

"Hush," Elizabeth Smith soothed. "He'll be back. He'll bring us food."

There was only the sixteen-year-old boy to manage the raft. The women couldn't help much. There were four small children to watch each moment they were away from the bank. Mrs. Polk stayed with her husband in the wagon bed. He was delirious now, burning with fever.

They made less than a mile that day, then tied up at the bank. The children cried for food but finally were quiet. Even the baby was asleep, and Elizabeth Smith climbed up to the forward wagon bed to comfort Mr. Polk.

The next day she wrote in her diary:

The waves go over the raft and icicles hang from the wagon beds to the water. Last night, Adam Polk expired. No one was with him but his wife and myself. We sat up all night with him while the waves were dashing below.

They remained tied to the bank that day and the next. They had no choice. On this stretch of the river they were facing the full sweep of the wind. They wrapped Adam Polk's body in a blanket and placed it under a canvas on the lee side of the raft.

The second night, at dusk, Cornelius Smith staggered in from the storm. He was completely exhausted from his struggle over rocks and through ice-incrusted brush. Weak as he was, he brought fifty pounds of beef.

He also brought good news—and bad.

"Welch and the boys are down below," he told his wife weakly. "And the cows."

"Are the boys all right?"

"Yeah. They had a tough time of it up there in the snow. But Welch brought 'em through."

"Bless his heart! . . . Now get over here by the stove. Get those wet shoes off. Here—I'll help you. . . . Did they go hungry too?"

"They killed the red heifer. I grabbed this hunk and lit right out, knowing you all were starving. . . . A feller's running a small ferryboat down there, fetching cattle across the river. But we got to wait our turn. And we got to wait our turn hauling around the Cascades. . . . It don't look too good, 'Lizabeth."

"We'll make it all right," Elizabeth Smith said with pretended confidence. "Now get those wet clothes off and wrap up in these blankets. I'll soon have some steaks frying."

"But there ain't enough boats waiting below the Cascades. We're the last outfit. Suppose we can't get a boat to take us down to the valley? We've got no money."

"We'll make it somehow. We're all safe and sound so far. . . . *Our* family, that is." She lowered her voice. "Poor Mrs. Polk!"

"How's Adam making out? Where are all the kids?"

"Sh-h. They're up there with her, keeping her company. She wanted to hold the baby. . . . Adam Polk died two nights ago."

"That's bad," Smith said. "Yeah, that's bad."

"As soon as these steaks are fried I'll have Mrs. Polk eat with us. It'll put new heart into her."

"I dunno, 'Lizabeth," her husband said wearily. "We're going to need a little luck."

The children slept soundly that night. Though Cornelius Smith was still weak, the next morning they got the raft out into the current. They could make no headway against the wind. The next day a lull came and they drifted down to the point where Welch and the boys were waiting their turn to ferry the cattle across.

While waiting—three days—they buried Adam Polk on the north bank of the river. It was a hard, desolate task. Only the grownups were there. On the way back to the raft, in the driving gloom, Cornelius Smith stumbled and fell. He was up at once, but he placed his hand on his wife's shoulder for support. She could feel his hand trembling.

"Sorry, honey," he said in a low voice. "Looks like I'm— kind of tuckered out."

"I know, but you'll get your strength back on the raft. It isn't far to the Cascades."

"I ain't sure I can handle that pole any more. The current's swift here. Welch has to stay with the cows. . . . We're cutting this mighty thin, 'Lizabeth."

"We're the last ones at the ferry," she pointed out. "Maybe we can persuade the ferryman to take us and the wagons down to the Cascades. He won't have any more customers this winter."

"Sounds good—if he'll do it. We already owe him for taking the cows across."

"Then we'll owe him some more. Our credit's good. Think of how much land we'll have in the valley!"

The ferryman agreed to the proposal and moved their whole outfit down to the Cascades. Here they assembled their wagons and prepared for the five-mile haul around the rapids. The road was cut into the bank and was composed of rocks and almost bottomless mud. Traffic had been heavy, and they were the last of the train.

They waited three days, and when their turn came the road was almost impassable. Mrs. Polk had gone on with another family. Smith and Welch had gone ahead with the cows, leaving the big boys to manage the oxen and wagon. Smith was eager to arrange for a boat below the Cascades to take them down to the valley.

So Elizabeth Smith, with her children and wagon, finally started over that lonely, storm-swept five miles. The oxen were so weak, the road so terrible, that everyone must walk. For the first time she wrote with a touch of desperation.

We start this morning around the portage. It rains and snows. I carry my babe and lead another through snow and water almost to my knees. I am afraid to look back for fear of seeing the wagon turn over. It is the worst road a team can possibly travel.

Each step was a struggle. In late afternoon the children collapsed from cold and fatigue. The oxen were exhausted. She had the boys unhitch and abandon the wagon, and the oxen carried the little children into the homestretch.

131

It was night when they got into camp below the Cascades. Smith was alone there. He had built a makeshift shelter—little more than a windbreak—and the family crept in one by one beside him. All were wet to the skin and chilled to the bone.

"You're a sight, honey," Cornelius Smith whispered. "But you fetched them through. . . . You left the wagon, eh?"

"We had to. Where are the boats?"

"Gone. There wasn't room for us. Welch has gone on with the cows. He says he'll be back with boats. . . . But I dunno, 'Lizabeth."

"He'll be back! He took care of the boys up there."

"What I mean, honey," Smith whispered, "I dunno what he'll find when he gets back here. I cain't get up."

That night was the worst of all. In the screaming blackness they couldn't go back after the wagon. They huddled behind their shelter while the hours dragged by. When it turned colder Elizabeth Smith, with her own body, protected her three youngest from the driving snow.

When daylight came Smith was too weak to move. Like a good horse driven too long, too hard, until its very heart is broken, he lay helpless in the mud. But Elizabeth Smith struggled on. She sent the boys back for the wagon. The oxen—a little stronger now—finally brought it through.

She got her family under the chill canvas, built a smoldering fire, and tried to make Smith comfortable. Welch would soon come with the boats. He must *surely* come. The third day passed, and the fourth. On the fifth day came Elizabeth Smith's first and only admission of defeat.

They had lived on beef alone for ten days past, and now there were only bones and remnants left. Through the great gap to the west, between gusts of snow, she had watched the river each day. There were no boats on the gray, tossing current. She had caught occasional glimpses of the valley, but its timbered hills were white and lifeless.

Her wagon was marooned below a great shoulder of rock which projected from the south wall. It was the very symbol of desolation, hung with wind-driven streamers of snow. A century later they were to call it Crown Point, and thousands of tourists would pause there to admire the view. They would lean against an artistic stone railing and look down eight hundred feet to the spot where Elizabeth Smith wrote:

It is almost an impossibility to cook and quite impossible to keep warm and dry. I froze or chilled my feet so that I cannot wear a shoe, so must go barefooted. The whole care of everything falls upon my shoulder. . . . I am not adequate to the task. . . .

Welch came back with the boats on the *ninth* day. He had been delayed by the storm. He had come as fast as he could. When he and his helpers scrambled up the icy bank it seemed that they had come to a lifeless camp. The oxen had been turned loose. The faded canvas wagon top and the heaped equipment near by were white with snow. Icicles hung from the spokes of the wagon wheels.

"Wait, men," Welch ordered. "Easy. I dunno what we got here."

"Look! There's smoke coming out of the stovepipe!"

"Somebody's still alive, at that! . . . Mis' Smith!" Welch called strongly. "Mis' Smith!"

Elizabeth Smith's distant voice replied: "Yes, Mr. Welch! We saw you coming—we're all ready! If you'll just give me a hand with my husband . . ."

"Sure, sure! He ain't—dead?"

"Of course not! He's just a little weak, that's all. Did you bring any—food?"

"Shore did! Plenty of it. Shall we stop to warm it up?"

"No," Elizabeth Smith said. "We'll eat it on the way. Let's get on to the valley."

They carried Smith down to the boats on an improvised litter. The others made it alone. Elizabeth Smith, in her matter-of-fact way—a little woman and very thin, but carrying her baby and leading her two-year-old, and the big boys bringing the others—walked through the snow, barefooted, to the boat.

"Look at that!" Welch whispered to his boatmen. "*Barefooted!* And not one of those kids missing! . . . Boys, I think —I'm gonna remember that picture!"

Yes, it was a picture. One of scores, hundreds, shining briefly but bravely on the dimming mirror of the past. And on November 27, just twenty-five days after leaving The Dalles—six months and twenty days after leaving the Missouri—Elizabeth Smith, her husband, and her seven children made it safely to the valley.

1845

In the fall of 1845, many emigrant trains were halted at The Dalles, with no way to descend the Columbia gorge. It could only be done by boat or raft, and timber for rafts was increasingly hard to find. A few boats were available for hire but at enormous cost. The boat speculators had a perfect monopoly. Winter was close. The few settlers who had money couldn't quibble over prices. It was cross the mountains or die.

For those who had no money and no means of building rafts the situation was desperate. Out of that desperation came the courage to attempt what was presumed to be impossible: haul wagons over the mile-high Cascades. Many trains tried it and failed. One succeeded and made history. It broke the monopoly in the gorge. It enabled the wagons, finally, to go all the way from the Missouri to the free land in the valley.

XI

THE BARLOW TRAIL

ON SEPTEMBER 30, 1845, William Rector arrived at The Dalles with his wife, seven children, and the usual ox-drawn wagon, household goods, and cattle.

He found a deplorable condition at the head of the gorge. Emigrants who had neither money nor rafts were milling there like angry waters backed up behind a dam. Rector's own outlook was bad. His food was almost gone and he had no money. His family would be starving before he could get a raft built.

Rector took in the situation at a glance. He was a raw-boned, deliberate man of grim appearance but with a gloomy twinkle in his eye. He had no fear of desert, mountain, or man. He had no patience with men who boasted too much, or made excuses, or pretended virtues they didn't possess. A spade was always a spade with William Rector.

He hailed a boat speculator who was waiting like a vulture on the rocks.

"My name's Rector. Bill Rector. Your boat for hire?"

"Yep."

"I've got no money. Do you give an honest man credit?"

The speculator shifted his quid of tobacco and spat into the current. "Nope."

"Well, I've got some milk cows. Maybe we can make a deal."

"How many cows?"

"Eight. I shore hate to part with any of them. I *got* to get down to the valley."

"Where are your cows?"

"Over yonder. Back of the wagon with the white oxen."

The speculator studied the cows. "They're in mighty poor flesh. All right—it's a deal. You'll have to wait three weeks before I can take your outfit down. Meantime——"

"Three *weeks?*" Rector repeated. "We haven't got food enough. We can't wait that long."

"You'll wait. You ain't in Missouri now, friend. . . . Meantime you drive them cows down to below the rapids. I'll take delivery there. See that none of them breaks a leg on the way."

"Just a minute!" Rector said, scowling. "You want *all* my cows?"

"Yep."

"For freighting my outfit fifty miles? After I've walked those cows clean across the plains?"

"Yep."

"The deal's off, then! I'll keep the cows."

The speculator shrugged. "Suit yourself. Maybe you'd like to try the mountains?"

"Maybe I will."

"They're only a mile high. You'll be back. When you do, and come crying around here for boats——"

"And right now," William Rector said, "you can stop grinning like that, mister! Rob these folks blind if you've a mind to! Don't you set there like a blasted buzzard——"

"All right, all right," the speculator said hastily. "No offense, friend. No offense."

That night, in a towering rage, Rector started for the mountains. Others were ahead, attempting to scale the barrier south of Mount Hood. He followed the wagon tracks easily as he mounted through the timber.

Two weeks later, on the summit, just south of the overpowering bulk of Mount Hood, two men stood side by side, looking west. It was early morning. Their wagons were still

far below in the thinning timber. These two had gone ahead
to find out, if possible, if wagons could descend the westward
slope.

One was Samuel K. Barlow, a heavy-set man with a confident, expansive manner. The other was Joel Palmer, a gaunt
Missourian.

The view westward was magnificent. Fifty miles distant,
five thousand feet lower, the sunlight glittered on the broad,
well-watered valley. It seemed to stretch into infinity, like a
shoreless sea. Near at hand was the unbroken forest, falling
in giant swells that broke quickly into deep canyons. It
looked like fairly easy going, yet many cliffs and impassable
ravines could be hidden down there.

"We can get the wagons up here to the summit, Barlow,"
Joel Palmer said. "But what's below?"

"Nothing but timber!" Barlow said with his usual confidence. "We can hack a trail through it."

"I dunno. We'd ought to look it over first."

"Let's take a chance! We'll find a way! God didn't make
mountains without leaving a place to cross them."

"Talk sense, man!" Palmer said, annoyed. "We *can't* take
a chance. Too many folks back there are depending on us
to give them the right answer."

"Sam Barlow's always given his train the right answer so
far!"

"Maybe so, but you've never met up with mountains like
this. Come on, let's give it a look down there."

"Tell you what, Joel," Barlow countered. "You go down
and I'll get back to camp. The folks might as well be bringing the wagons up to the summit."

"And give Sam Barlow a chance to rest his feet, eh? All
right, run along. I'd ought to be back by sundown."

It was long after sundown when Joel Palmer returned. His
clothes were in shreds and his moccasined feet bleeding.
The next morning he gathered the men of the train together

and told them the bad news: the way was impassable westward. The country was rough beyond description, and a final "big canyon" barred the way. It was two thousand feet deep, not vertical, but so nearly so that wagons would have to be lowered with tackle. They had no tackle. Meantime, winter was not far away—particularly up there at the summit.

Barlow, as usual, was unconvinced.

"We can take wagons anywhere! The canyon can't be that deep!"

"There's a difference between you and me, Barlow," Palmer said. "*I* saw the canyon."

"But we've got to go on! We can't go back to The Dalles. Things are in an awful shape there. Where's that man Rector who got in from The Dalles last night?"

"Here," Rector answered from the edge of the crowd.

"Step up here, Rector. . . . This is Joel Palmer. You already know me, probably—Captain Samuel K. Barlow."

"Yes, sir. Howdy, Mr. Palmer."

"Now, Rector," Barlow directed, "tell Palmer about The Dalles. Tell them what we're up against!"

"Yes, sir. . . . It's shore bad, Mr. Palmer. There's maybe five hundred folks waiting there now, and more wagons coming in every day. Half of them will have to winter there. The mission's plumb out of food. I figure Barlow's right—we better go over the mountain."

"But doggone it, Barlow hasn't even seen the canyon on the other side!"

"He will, Mr. Palmer," Rector said quietly, "if you folks agree to a proposition I got to make. We'll naturally expect Mr. Barlow to take a lead in it."

Barlow beamed. "You can always depend on Sam Barlow! What's your proposition?"

Joel Palmer liked this man Rector. He liked the gloomy twinkle in his eye—particularly when Rector looked at Sam Barlow. Rector's proposition was simple. Why not take the

140

wagons up to the summit and use that as a base to attack whatever lay below? If it *was* impossible to take the wagons farther, leave them at the summit until spring and take the women, children, and livestock out on foot. Meanwhile, two good men could hurry on to the valley and get help from the settlers—packhorses, equipment, and food—and return to meet the train.

The whole company debated this proposal. Barlow was enthusiastic.

"Good! You've hit the nail right on the head, Rector! It's just the way I figured it!"

"But if we leave the wagons at the summit," Palmer asked, "who'll look out for them all winter? The Indians'll steal anything they can get their hands on."

Rector had already thought of that. "There's six men in the outfit that came along with me, Mr. Palmer. They've agreed to stay with the wagons till spring, provided we guarantee to see their women and children safely to the settlement."

"Fine!" Barlow shouted. "Fine! Certainly we'll guarantee it!"

"Don't you tell them that, Mr. Barlow," Rector said gravely. "Best leave the guaranteeing to me. . . . It'll probably take two weeks to get the wagons up to the summit. By that time the two of us who've gone ahead should be back again with help."

"You mean those two should start out today?"

"Right now," Rector said. "As soon as we've all agreed."

It was soon agreed. The plan was reasonable. It was decided that the two advance scouts should travel light—just their blankets and a tarp and enough food to get them to the valley.

"Mr. Barlow," Rector asked, "how long do you figure it would take two good men to get to the valley?"

"Two days—three at the most. You can *see* the valley from

the summit. . . . You'll want to be one of the two to go ahead, of course, Rector. Who do you want to go along with you?"

"I've been studying about that. It'll be hard going down there—new country and all. I'd ought to have a good man."

"There's plenty of good men in *my* train," Barlow boasted. "Take anybody you want!"

"That's fine, Mr. Barlow," Rector said. "And I've done picked him out. Ever since I joined this outfit last night I've been hearing how good a man he is. He's always willing to take a chance. He thrives on danger and hardship. I'd shore feel proud to have him along."

"Who is he? Name him!"

"His name, sir, is Barlow. Captain Samuel K. Barlow."

There was a general shout of laughter and approval.

"Now wait," Barlow protested. "Just a second, now——"

"Of course it would be you, Sam," Palmer cut in. "Think of it—you'll get to see the canyon before the rest of these lads. And you and Rector will be the first to blaze a trail to the settlement. Explorers, b'gosh!"

"But I've got my train—I've got responsibilities——"

"Now don't you fret about that," Palmer soothed. "All we'll be doing is hacking a road up to the summit. Your wagons will make out. You go right along with him, Sam. We wouldn't think of cheating you out of the chance, not for a minute!"

So Rector and Samuel K. Barlow were elected to descend through the trackless forests and make their way to the settlements. In spite of Rector's sardonic humor, theirs was a truly grim responsibility. The welfare of the whole train depended upon their making it safely through.

Years later, when William Rector was one of the leading citizens of the valley—proprietor of one of its first woolen mills and head of other substantial interests—he wrote an account of that trip with Barlow. He cautiously refrained from putting down all that occurred, but he recorded enough

to create a vivid picture of the manner in which men of opposite temperaments face hardship and death.

Barlow himself—though none too pleased with some of
Rector's anecdotes—later referred to Rector's own account as
convincing proof that he had personally scouted what was
to become a famous trail.

Concerning the start of his adventure, Rector wrote:

We started that morning at daylight, with only two days' ra-
tions, which was supposed to be ample. Barlow and Palmer had
been high on Mount Hood so as to overlook all the mountains
and see the valley, but they were not competent to judge distances
from such a height. We found to our sorrow that it took six days
to reach Oregon City.

It was a terrific six days. The first day was uneventful; they
merely developed a hearty appetite. Barlow remarked that
he could eat all his food for supper that night but made what
Rector records gravely as a very sensible proposition—that
they should eat only half their remaining food at each meal.
In that way they would always have food, no matter how
long it took to get to the valley.

The second day they descended into the "big canyon." A
cold, misty rain fell all day, and when darkness came they
were wet to the skin and thoroughly chilled. They tried to
start a fire, but their matches were wet. They tried to use
their gun priming—Rector was carrying a light shotgun—but
with no success.

Barlow, shivering and miserable, was convinced they were
done for.

"We'll never hold out till morning, Rector! We'll never get
out of here!"

"Big canyon, ain't it?"

"We've got to have a fire! What are we going to do?"

"First, we get our matches dry," Rector told him reassur-
ingly. "See that big log over there? We both get straddle of
it. We take a dry limb and both get holt of it . . ."

Facing each other on the log, each grasping the dry limb, and with a blanket over them to keep the place dry, they rubbed violently on the log until a spot was warm. They placed their wet matches on this spot, and they were soon dry enough to kindle a fire. Very briefly Rector states what happened next:

"I worked all night getting wood and keeping fire. Barlow slept."

After a scanty breakfast they started out again and for several hours followed the canyon to the south. The rain had stopped, but a heavy fog hung low over the dripping timber. Their surroundings were gloomy beyond description. The forests and mountains seemed endless.

Barlow was sure they were at the edge of the valley, but the country grew rougher at every forward step. Finally Rector called a halt.

"We're getting nowhere, Barlow. We can't depend on the lay of the land any more, so we're traveling by compass from now on. And we're traveling north."

"North?" Barlow said, shivering. "Isn't the valley west?"

"But the river's closer. We'll meet up with somebody driving cattle along the south bank."

"But the mountain's in the way!"

"Sure. But we're going around the mountain."

It was easier said than done. Working northward, they were forced to climb over terrificly rough terrain. Finally they were above the fog, with the bulk of Mount Hood looming tremendously at their right. They circled the base and were forced to scale a great icy cliff.

At the top Barlow was sure they were back at their starting point, with the wagon camp less than a mile away. Actually, the bulk of the mountain lay between; and Rector, in short-tempered mood, told Barlow harshly to obey orders and follow along.

Barlow did so, but he was losing heart. He fell often on

the rough ground. Rector carried most of the equipment, but Barlow steadily grew weaker. Both were almost starved. On the fourth day, as they plodded doggedly along, Barlow was completely dispirited.

"Mr. Rector!" he called weakly from the rear.

"Yeah?"

"If I was to fall down and break my leg, what would you do with me?"

"I'd eat you, doggone it!"

Later, looking back, Rector saw to his astonishment that Barlow was weeping bitterly.

"What are you crying about? Why, Barlow, you old fool— *I* won't eat you. You ain't going to break any leg. Don't you give up now. We'll make it to the river by tomorrow."

"We'll never make it!" Barlow wailed. "We're done for! Mr. Rector . . ."

"What now?"

"If I fall down and hurt myself so I can't walk, please take the ax and knock my brains out. I don't want to linger in pain. Will you promise?"

"Take care you don't fall down!" Rector told him. "Get holt of yourself, Barlow. Remember those women and children waiting back there. We'll make it!"

The next morning they made it to the river. There they met an emigrant party driving cattle along the south bank, below the Cascades. Rested and refreshed, they stayed with this party and made it to Oregon City without further adventure.

A party of settlers was soon organized. They went up to the summit and first brought the women and children down. Then they lowered the wagons into the canyon one by one, anchoring with ropes to the tough mountain laurel. Below, the train re-formed and made it laboriously through the descending timber ahead of the winter snow.

That same fall, however, some daring, desperate emigrant

—a hero whose name is now lost in the crowded history of the trail—brought his oxen and wagon down that terrific two-thousand-foot drop "all in one piece." Winter was breathing on his back. He had to try it. He did it by locking his wheels, tying a forty-foot fir tree behind the wagon as a drag—hitching to the small end of the tree so that the branches would dig like claws into the face of the slope—then zigzagging back and forth until he reached the bottom.

News of this exploit soon spread over the valley. It reached the alert ears of Samuel K. Barlow, and when the Provisional Legislature met that winter a historic item was on the agenda.

"Gentlemen, this request is one we should take pleasure in granting. Here is a man who did what others said couldn't be done—he brought wagons up the east slope of the mighty Cascades. He was the first to stand at the summit and look boldly westward and say with confidence: '*That* is the way.' He was the one who said, while others doubted, 'Wagons *can* go through.' He was the first to scout that trail, pitting his puny strength but giant heart against the awesome wilderness!

"Gentlemen, I move you that we grant a franchise for the first toll road in the Oregon Country to the man who made that road possible—that hero of the trail, that man of mighty vision—*Samuel K. Barlow!*"

Thus the Barlow Trail came into being.

As to who could rightly claim discovery is immaterial. Its historic importance is that this first road across the five-hundred-mile length of the Cascades—the roughest, muddiest, most boulder-strewn haul west of the Missouri—was a godsend to hundreds of emigrant trains during the next two decades. To that extent—and for building and managing the road, and for charging reasonable tolls—Samuel K. Barlow was entitled to credit. Even William Rector would occasionally admit that.

1847 – 1848

On November 20, 1847, at Whitman's mission east of the Cascades, occurred one of the most brutal Indian massacres in the history of the West. The mission was destroyed by the marauding Cayuses. Dr. and Mrs. Whitman and ten others were killed, and sixty-two white persons were kept prisoner by the Indians until ransomed by the Hudson's Bay Company almost a month later.

The atrocious crime aroused the American settlement. The Provisional Government at once organized a regiment of riflemen to proceed against the Cayuses. At the same time it was decided to send a messenger to Washington with an urgent appeal for territorial status for Oregon and for immediate military aid. If the Whitman massacre went unpunished there was grave danger of a concerted Indian uprising.

But Washington was more than three thousand miles away. Who in the settlement could hope to survive that midwinter dash across the continent? Seasoned frontiersmen said it couldn't be done.

Governor Abernethy selected Joseph L. Meek—ex-mountain man, survivor of numberless hair-raising adventures—to make the formidable, forlorn attempt.

XII

THE LUCK OF JOE MEEK

To JOSEPH L. MEEK, drinker of hard liquor, the headiest draught of all was public notice. When the Oregon Country settlers decided he was the man to attempt the thirty-two-hundred mile midwinter dash to Washington to plead for military aid against the Indians responsible for the Whitman massacre, Joe was in his glory.

For days he rode his white horse about the settlement, displaying the memorial he was commissioned to deliver in person to President Polk. A confident, swashbuckling air surrounded him. Unquestionably Joe Meek was the man of the hour!

Belatedly he began to plan the trip. Under his love of dramatics was a wolfish strain of realism, and he knew the chances were remote that any living man could make it alone across the snow-choked Rockies and the immensity of the drifted plains. What he needed was a durable companion willing to brave the dangers and death that lurked beside each mile of the bitter trail ahead.

He decided on "Squire" Ebberts, a prosperous settler near Champoeg. By contrast to Meek's strapping physique and robust manner, Ebberts was a small, quiet man, as careful of money as Joe was spendthrift. Nevertheless, he was as tough-fibered as Joe himself and intensely patriotic.

Joe found him splitting rails in the dreary winter rain. Ebberts had taken no part in the noisy settlers' meetings following the massacre. He had kept on working at his homestead, ready to be called when needed.

149

He leaned on his ax and listened to Joe's plea that he go along on the hazardous journey. Knowing Joe Meek, he was under no delusions about the part he was expected to play. If they failed to make it through to Washington it would be Joe Meek who died a hero's death. If they succeeded Joe Meek would get the credit.

"So that's the way she sets up, Squire," Joe concluded enthusiastically. "They done picked me to carry this memorial to Washington. I'm entitled to call myself 'envoy extraordinary from the Republic of Oregon.'" Joe had invented this title himself. "Ain't that something? *Envoy extraordinary!*"

"Not minister plenipotentiary?" Ebberts asked with a gloomy twinkle.

"How's that?" Joe's ears fairly quivered. "Minister pleni—what?"

"Never mind. So you want me to go along, Joe. It'll be a tough trip."

"Shore, but we'll make it. We got to, Squire! The United States has got to be on the job! Are we gonna sit here and let those Indians slaughter our womenfolks and children——"

"I know," Ebberts said with a sigh. "I know, Joe. We've got to do it. It means I'll be gone from the farm until next fall, at least. It'll cost me plenty."

"The United States Government'll take care of us!" Joe promised grandly. "It's only right! Joe Meek'll guarantee that!"

"And you'll take care of me, eh?"

"Why, shore! Ain't we in this fifty-fifty all the way?"

"Good," Ebberts said. "Let's start right now. They gave you five hundred dollars expense money, didn't they? Fork over half of it, Joe."

"Half the five hundred?" Joe was a little nonplused. "Oh yes—that five hundred. Well—er—the fact is, Squire, I've done spent it. I had to get a trail outfit together."

"Costing maybe a hundred dollars. Where's the rest of it?"

"Well—I had to buy some knickknacks for my squaw, didn't I? And the kids?"

"And how much whisky for the boys?"

"Well, doggone it," Joe complained, "when a man's going on a long trip, ain't he entitled——"

"Sure. Now listen, Joe. If we make it through and there's glory in it, just you wallow in it. If there's speeches to be made, you make them. But *if* they vote us expense money in Washington——"

"You'll get your share!" Joe promised. "I'll guarantee that! When Joe Meek goes partners with a man——"

"Just see that you do," Ebberts cut in. "If you don't, there'll be a new hide nailed up right on this barn. It'll be Joe Meek's —with the ears missing."

"Why, Squire!"

"Get along," Ebberts told him. "I'll see you at Oregon City tomorrow, Joe. See that you're sober."

They didn't actually get under way until January 4, 1848. All the Indians in the interior were now on the warpath, and Meek and Ebberts had to wait at The Dalles until a company of riflemen could escort them as far as the Blue Mountains.

On the way upriver from The Dalles the company paused at the ruins of Whitman's mission. There Joe Meek helped in a grim and terrible task. It was to bury what remained of the twelve men, women, and children killed in the massacre almost two months before. Catholic priests had covered the bodies hurriedly in shallow graves. But wolves had passed that way, and little more than skeletons were left.

Ebberts didn't have the heart for it, but Joe Meek labored like a madman, helping to dig deep, permanent resting places. With his own hands he laid the bones of two little girls side by side and covered them with one of his own blankets. They still had ribbons in their hair. When they rode away into the storm Ebberts saw what few living men had ever seen: tears blinding the eyes of Joe Meek.

151

Ebberts spoke of that moment later, in their snowbound camp beyond the Blue Mountains. Five other wandering white men had joined them, but Ebberts and Meek camped alone. When they were muffled in their blankets, in utter darkness, Ebberts said:

"I could see it kind of got you, Joe, back there at the mission. I recollect now that you'd met the Whitmans some years back. That was why it cut you so deep?"

"No. The Whitmans were fine folks. But that ain't why."

"I know," Ebberts said gently. "It was on account of those two little girls. Two little white girls—killed by those blasted Indians!"

"No," Joe said. "They were both half-breeds, Squire."

"You knew them?"

"Yeah. By the ribbons in their hair. I sent them ribbons up to the mission last Christmas."

"Well! I wouldn't have thought you had that much sentiment, Joe."

"This is between us, Squire," Joe said. "The one with the blue ribbon was Jim Bridger's gal. He sent her over to the mission to get her schooling. I buried her for Jim."

"Hm-m. And the other one?"

"The other one's name—the one with the red ribbon—was Helen. Her mother was a Shoshone gal—the daughter of a chief and the purtiest and bravest little squaw that ever rode the mountains. She died when Helen was three years old. Her dad took Helen over to the mission so she'd have the right—fetching up."

"You knew him—Helen's father?"

"Yeah. A no-account critter. Plumb worthless. But he'll shore make those Cayuses pay for what they done at the mission! You can bank on that, Squire!"

"Who *is* her dad?"

"His name is Joseph L. Meek."

The snow was deep beyond the Blue Mountains. The wind

howled across the rocky wastes bordering the Snake. Two of their five companions stayed at Fort Boise, but Meek and the others pushed on. Joe was now wearing the distinctive red belt and Canadian cap of the Hudson's Bay *voyageurs*. Ebberts thought this a touch of vanity until they encountered a large war party of Bannocks.

The painted warriors surrounded the five white men and moved in for the kill. Then they saw Meek's cap and red belt and decided to parley. Meek told them he was on Hudson's Bay business and that a large party of Hudson's Bay men were close behind, bringing plenty of trade goods. This appealed both to the caution and greed of the Bannocks, and they permitted the five to ride on.

When the driving snow hid the renegades Ebberts gave a great sigh of relief.

"That was a close shave, Joe. You're a good poker player."

"You got to run a bluff once in a while," Joe returned carelessly. "Sometimes it works."

"It was lucky you were wearing that belt and cap."

"Oh, shore. Nice outfit, ain't it? Let's show a little speed, boys. We got to make it to Fort Hall. By tomorrow those Bannocks are likely to be annoyed."

They stopped only for a good meal at Fort Hall, then Ebberts and Meek pushed on alone. They were now in the driving snow and bitter cold of the high plateau. Their horses bogged down in the mounting drifts, but Meek fortunately knew how to make snowshoes from the willows, so they abandoned their horses and went on afoot.

Progress was slow in the swirling gloom. Their food gave out, and for two days they went hungry. On the third day Meek was lucky: he shot two polecats. They ate them and were able to make it to the headwaters of Bear River. There they certainly would have perished had they not happened to stumble upon the winter camp of an old friend of Meek's, a notorious character named Peg-Leg Smith.

Peg-Leg and Meek greeted each other with howls of delight. Peg-Leg slaughtered a fat cow and they had a feast. They caroused all night. They rested the next day, and when they pushed on, refreshed, they had all the food they could carry.

Meek took all this in his stride, but a light had begun to dawn on Ebberts.

"Joe, it was lucky you knew old Peg-Leg, wasn't it?"

"Oh, shore. Remind me to tell you some yarns about that mangy critter. I got a barrel of 'em."

"And making those snowshoes, and happening to shoot those two polecats—that was just luck too?"

"Well, weren't they fat polecats? Brother, you can eat worse! I remember, once, over in the Comanche country——"

"All right, all right! I'm not complaining." Ebberts chuckled. "I was just figuring out about this luck business."

It was the same way at Fort Bridger. When old Jim Bridger learned of the chore Meek had done at Whitman's mission with his own hands, the fort was theirs. When they left they were no longer afoot: they were riding Jim Bridger's best mules. Strapped behind their saddles was much food supplied by Jim Bridger.

It was always a question of food, of eternal snow and bitter cold, of daily, hourly struggle for survival. They came to the backbone of the Rockies and fought on toward the Sweetwater. This was the deepest snow of all and the loneliest stretch of the continent.

They lost their mules one by one. Their provisions gave out. Their strength dwindled. It seemed this *was* the end. . . . Then Meek happened to find a lone buffalo—snow-covered, statuesque, but still alive—left behind by some grazing summer herd.

They killed the buffalo and found the meat tough and lean, but they dined like kings. As they enjoyed the feast by a glowing fire, in the shelter of drifts piling up behind their windbreak, Ebberts smiled for the first time in bitter days.

"How come you found that buffalo, Joe? Just plain luck?"

"Oh, shore," Joe said, chewing with gusto. "If a feller lives the right kind of life and don't work too hard and keeps his eyes open, he's bound to come out all right. I remember, once, down by the big salt lake, me and Kit Carson and a couple other pilgrims . . ." This story went far into the night.

The buffalo meat took them to the Platte. They struggled on to Fort Laramie, and when they staggered into the palisade they found a trader in charge who happened to know Meek. When they left they were well fed, well equipped, and had fresh mules to ride—and in a blinding snowstorm they rode directly into a camp of five hundred Sioux.

It was too late to retreat: they were surrounded by great snow-whitened tepees. If a single alert warrior had happened to peer out into the storm—if a single dog had barked—it would have been the end. The man who happened to see them first was the only white man in the enormous encampment—a Frenchman named LeBean.

LeBean beckoned them silently into his tent. He had heard of the great Joe Meek. Though he was risking his life and that of his squaw, LeBean escorted them through the camp and on into the safety of the storm.

Several days later they came to the beginning of the homestretch: the wind-swept and icebound Missouri. For the first time Ebberts permitted himself a gleam of hope.

"Joe," he said that night, wonderingly, as they camped in the protection of the Missouri's north bank, "it looks like we might make it!"

"Why, shore!" Joe said in surprise. "It ain't but a couple hundred miles to St. Joe. You had any doubts about it, Squire?"

"Well—we needed plenty of that Joe Meek luck."

"Sho! This ain't been a bad trip. You should have seen me

and Milton Sublette one time, up in the Tetons. We were afoot, we had no victuals, and after I'd carried Sublette on my back for eight days——"

"Now wait," Ebberts said with a sigh. "Why carry him on your back?"

"His leg was broke! And him a potbellied critter weighing two hundred and fifty pounds! D'ye know what shape my feet was in when we finally got to camp? Well, sir, I set ol' Sublette down and took a look. I'd been wondering why I'd been sinking to my ankles at each step, and now I see why. All I had left was ankles! For the last forty miles my feet had been worn off clean to the instep!"

"Now, now!" Ebberts reproved. "*Mister* Meek!"

"And you," Joe said pityingly, "wondering if we'd make it to St. Joe!"

They made it to St. Joseph, Missouri, just sixty-two days after leaving the valley—the fastest trip yet made across the plains, and in the dead of winter. But they were still far from Washington—emaciated, penniless, dressed in ragged and grimy mountain clothing. How could they even get down to St. Louis?

"We could use a little cash now, Joe," Ebberts said gloomily as they plodded into the snowbound frontier town. "I wish you'd saved some of that five-hundred-dollar expense money."

"Sho, we don't need money! Ain't I the envoy extraordin—— *Wait* a minute! What was that triple-geared word you pulled out of the hat back there in Oregon? Minister—what?"

"Minister plenipotentiary. . . . I was only joshing, Joe. You can't——"

"I shore can! Minister plenipotentiary!" Meek's sunken features lighted. "Squire, we'll ride that critter clean to Washington!"

And they did so—literally. A gentleman at St. Joseph was so impressed that he drove them in his personal carriage to Independence. The first steamer took them down-river

without charge to St. Louis. There Meek wired President
Polk that they were on their way. The President courteously
wired in reply, urging him to hurry on to Washington.

The St. Louis papers headlined the event. The two Oregonians became famous overnight. The President's wire, plus
the papers he bore—plus Meek's wild garb and impressive
manner—took him and Ebberts all the way to the nation's
capital without cost.

In Washington, Meek insisted on going to the best hotel,
where he attracted tremendous attention. He ate a huge meal,
then ordered a carriage, and loudly demanded to be driven to
the White House. Ebberts was terrified.

"We can't do this, Joe! We can't go to the White House
in this getup!"

"We shore can! What ails you, Squire? You rode through
that hostile Sioux camp without turning a hair!"

"But we can't call on the President like this—ragged,
dirty——"

"Listen, Squire," Joe said. It was one of his rarely grave
moments. "How was Doc Whitman dressed when we buried
him? We'll make it, son. We're riding our luck plumb to the
finish."

Joe Meek's luck held to the finish. They were ushered into
a large and elegant office, that of secretary to the President.
Many distinguished gentlemen were waiting there. The secretary barely glanced at his outlandish visitors and told them
to wait. Ebberts shrank into a corner, but Joe Meek strode
impatiently about the richly carpeted room. He hadn't fought
starvation and death across the continent—aye, and buried his
dead—to be brushed off by this pink-cheeked secretary.

Abruptly he exploded:

"Listen, boy!" His bellow brought distant guards to attention. "I've come a long ways to see President Polk! My business is important!"

The secretary eyed him coldly. "I *beg* your pardon?"

"You heard me, *garsong!* Tell the President that a gentleman from Oregon is waiting to see him. It's about life and death and massacres and war—and there's no time to be lost. Shake a leg, now!"

"My dear sir! . . . Wait—you're from Oregon? You're Joe Meek?"

"Who else, ye dim-wit?"

The secretary arose and extended his hand. "Why, Uncle Joe—this is a pleasure! I'm your nephew—Knox Walker."

"Knox Walker? You're Aggie's boy, Knox?" Joe threw back his head and laughed. "Ho! I might have known it! Trust a Meek to pick himself a soft roost like this! How are ye, boy?"

"I'll tell the President immediately, Uncle Joe. Just a moment."

Yes, the secretary was a nephew of Joe Meek's, though they had never met before. Within twenty minutes the office was cleared. All the President's appointments were canceled for the day. Knox Walker threw open the big door, bowing.

"All right, Uncle Joe. And Mr. Ebberts. This way, please."

Ebberts shrank back. "I cain't do it, Joe. You go in. I'll wait out here."

"No, you don't! Come on, Squire! Doggone it, weren't you with me when the going was toughest? Get up from there!"

"Well——"

"All right, son," Joe said loudly. "We're a-coming."

So Joe Meek and Squire Ebberts—ex-mountain men, citizens of the Willamette Valley, messengers of destiny—walked through the door; and a gray, grim man behind a big desk arose to meet them smilingly.

"Mr. President," said Knox Walker. "The gentlemen from Oregon."

The conference with President Polk brought prompt results. The next day an urgent message went to Congress calling for immediate creation of the Territory of Oregon. Congress began its debate on the measure. Historic wheels were in motion.

Ebberts wanted to withdraw quietly from Washington, their mission accomplished, but Meek was in the spotlight now and loved it. As the protégé of the President and the uncle of Knox Walker he was the social lion of the capital. He was soon calling influential senators by their first names. Wealthy politicians kept him supplied with funds. Why hurry back to Oregon?

So Ebberts started West alone. Being penniless—and without Joe Meek—he had to work his way back to Oregon. Eighteen months after leaving the valley he arrived at his Champoeg home, ragged and footsore. He found his farm in run-down condition and immediately went to work.

While he was plowing one sweltering day he looked up through eyes half blinded with perspiration and saw a gorgeous horseman looking down at him smilingly. The horseman wore gauntlets of hand-tooled leather. His jacket, saddle, and boots were spotless. Upon his breast was the shining shield of a United States marshal. It was Joe Meek.

"Hi thar, Squire!" Joe boomed. "I heard you were back!"

"Whoa, Sam! Whoa, Whitey!" Ebberts halted his oxen and leaned against the plow handles. "Hello, Joe."

"What took you so long, you old blizzard buster? Things have shore been happening around here. We're the Territory of Oregon now! And who nailed up the proclamation down to Oregon City? Why, the first U.S. marshal of this said territory. Ol' Joe Meek, of course!"

Ebberts nodded. "I heard about it. I'm glad you came along, Joe. I've been waiting to ask you——"

"You should have stayed in Washington with me, Squire! I was wined and dined till I was blue in the face. Speeches? Banquets? I wallowed in 'em! The pretty gals were thicker than jack rabbits. And when the President named General

159

Lane to be governor of the territory, *who* did they send out to Indiana——"

"I know—Joe Meek. What I wanted to ask you, Joe——"

"Listen! Me and the general came back by way of California, then up here by boat. As we sailed through the bay down there, d'ye know what happened? A U.S. sloop of war gave us a salute. Cannons, by gravy!" Joe guffawed loudly. "Between us, Squire, that salute was for the general, but was it Joe Meek's fault he happened to be standing on the poop deck, so *he* had to take the bow?"

"No, it was just plain luck," Ebberts said. "Listen to *me*, Joe. Did Congress vote you any expense money back there?"

"Why, shore! Ten thousand dollars, Squire! Around three thousand of it had to go to Judge Thornton, of course. You remember, he went to Washington around the Horn before that Whitman business."

"Where's the rest of it?"

"The rest of it?" Joe blinked uneasily. "Oh, you mean what was left."

"That's just what I mean—the seven thousand that was left. You were going to take care of me, fifty-fifty—remember?"

"Oh, yeah. . . . Why—um—the fact is, Squire——" Joe's horse began to edge away. "Well, doggone it, you know how it is in Washington. Every time you stop to scratch your back—— Now wait, Squire! You'll get your share. I'm gonna put in a claim for more expense money. As soon as it comes through——"

"Listen, Joe——"

But Joe was already wheeling his horse. "Well, I got to get along. You and me made history, didn't we, Squire? Doggoned if we didn't! Come over and see me at Oregon City. I'll introduce you to the general. I shore will!"

"Hold on, now!" Ebberts said. "Wait a second, Meek!"

But Meek was thundering away, a gloved hand upraised. "So long, Squire!"

"Why, that——!" Ebberts got hold of himself with an effort. He shook his head, mimicking Joe's grand manner: "'We made history, didn't we, Squire? Come over and I'll introduce you to the general.' Oh well." He smiled a little with resignation and shook the plow handles. "Giddap, Whitey! Get along, Sam! Get along, now!"

1848 – 1849

Joe Meek cut quite a swath in Washington during the historic summer of 1848. On the face of it he was the leading spokesman for the Oregon Country settlers in the bitter congressional battle which ended in the creation of the Oregon Territory. When the spotlight of public notice was upon him Joe Meek was not one to step aside.

Actually, it was another Oregonian—a man of far different character from Joe Meek—who made history behind the scenes on that tremendous stage. His name was J. Quinn Thornton, a gaunt and scholarly settler who had been sent to Washington before the Whitman massacre to lobby for the Oregon Bill.

These were times of grave portent on the national scene. The issue of slavery was coming to the front. The South was already arrayed against the North in thought. Men like Calhoun, Crittenden, and Douglas—and a homespun lawyer from Illinois, Abraham Lincoln—were beginning their imprint on history.

Among these giants, during stormy weeks, moved the inscrutable figure of J. Quinn Thornton. Whether by chance or design, accident or destiny, the man from Oregon crossed swords successfully with the shrewdest politicians of his time.

XIII

THE MAN FROM OREGON

COMMISSIONED by the Oregon Country settlers to lobby for territorial status in Washington, J. Quinn Thornton embarked on a trading ship from the Columbia River, sailed around the Horn, and reached the capital in the spring of 1848, two weeks ahead of Joe Meek.

Thornton was penniless and unknown, but he at once came to the attention of the master politicians. The "Oregon Question" had been a political football on the international scene for two decades. Though the treaty of 1846 had established the nation's northern boundary at the Forty-ninth parallel, the administration's belligerent and successful slogan—"Fifty-Four Forty or Fight"—was still fresh in memory.

The "Little Giant" of Illinois—Senator Stephen A. Douglas —was the first to sense the strategic capital to be made of this gaunt, unsmiling Oregonian. The day after Thornton appeared before the Senate Committee on Territories and Indian Lands, pleading his case in scholarly but unemotional fashion, Douglas dropped in casually at the office of the President to discuss administration strategy with the President's secretary, Knox Walker.

Douglas was a small man physically but possessed tremendous energy and personal charm. Knox Walker—young, ambitious, very sure of himself—was eager to impress the great Douglas with his grasp of capital affairs.

When Douglas proposed his plan Knox was dubious.

"You can't be serious, Senator! Naturally this man from

165

Oregon's in the public eye at the moment. Everybody admires those settlers, true. Thornton's a symbol of hardship, empire building—all that sort of thing. But make him a key man in *our* plans? Really, Mr. Douglas!"

Douglas beamed at him with the affection of an old gray wolf for a promising offspring. "Nevertheless, Walker, you'll give the President the benefit of my perhaps mistaken opinion?"

"Of course, sir. Your idea is to adopt Thornton at once and make him the voice of the administration?"

"On the Oregon Bill, yes. Let him rewrite it. Let him put in anything he wants, within reason."

"But why, Senator? What can he do for us?"

"He can win a battle for us, my boy. What do we need to trip up Calhoun? A crusade which will catch the public sympathy. Where is there a more appealing role than that of defender of the weak and helpless?"

Walker pursed his lips judiciously. "Hm-m. I'm beginning to see the pattern. It'll be *Thornton* who wants the anti-slavery clause in the Territorial Bill. It's his people—the noble settlers—who are asking Congress to make Oregon free ground!"

"Exactly."

"Which puts Calhoun and his crowd in the position of denying the settlers the right to choose for themselves!" Walker said with kindling enthusiasm. "So the slavery people will be fighting the noble settlers, not us!"

"Your stature's growing by the minute," Douglas assured him.

"You're right! I'll tell the President you're right! Unquestionably!"

"Your opinion flatters us both."

"And I'll talk to Thornton. We've got to be sure he sees eye to eye with us."

THE MAN FROM OREGON

"A word of advice on that point, Knox. Beware of these pious, simple-minded men."

"So that's Thornton's pose, is it?" Walker smiled. "I'll manage him. I've had experience with these horse traders."

"I'm sure you have," Douglas agreed. "Nevertheless, tread softly in his presence, my boy. I *think* this man Thornton is a type rarely seen along this section of the Potomac."

Within the week Thornton was invited to a conference with the President and his advisers. He arrived dressed in homespun and cowhide boots: a tall, bony man of inflexible dignity. Out in Oregon he was "Judge" Thornton—the first justice of the Provisional Government's Supreme Court—and he looked the part. No touch of humor ever lighted his craglike face. If he was impressed by his august company he gave no sign of it.

During their preliminary exchanges they weighed his utterances and found them lucid but colorless. The keenest eyes of the capital scrutinized his features but could probe no deeper than the outer mask of grim, rock-ribbed integrity. In the end, baffled, they invited him to rewrite the Territorial Bill.

Thornton at once took up the pen and wrote in the anti-slavery clause. The President and Douglas looked at each other, and the President nodded slightly. Douglas spoke in his most suave and impressive manner:

"You're aware, Judge Thornton, that there has been some controversy over the anti-slavery item?"

"I'm aware of it, Senator," Thornton replied.

"You understand that Calhoun will organize the entire South against it?"

"Perhaps."

"If it appears that Calhoun's opposition threatens the entire bill, would you be willing to compromise?"

"On the anti-slavery clause?"

"Yes."

"No," Thornton said.

There was a pause, then Douglas said: "I admire your bluntness, Judge Thornton. Permit an equally blunt question. Why not?"

Thornton's expressionless eyes studied him. "Because the settlers want the Oregon Territory to be free."

"My question appears to be answered," Douglas said. "Proceed, sir."

Thornton wrote in a second clause giving each Oregon settler a square mile of land. His third clause required two sections to be set aside in each township for school purposes.

Douglas again intervened.

"*Two* sections for school purposes, Judge? Isn't that rather generous? Heretofore we've only set aside one school section in each township."

"We want two in Oregon."

"And I gather, sir," said Douglas, amused, "that you Oregonians know what you want. But I'm afraid we'll hear from Calhoun on this!"

"I think not, Senator," Thornton replied.

Douglas shrugged. "I'm sure you know your own mind, Judge. Are you equally sure about Calhoun? What makes you think he won't object to the school clause?"

"He said so."

"You mean," Douglas said, "that you've already discussed this—the whole bill—with *Calhoun?*"

"Yes."

"Hm-m," Douglas said, his smile fading. "Who else was there?"

"Mr. Crittenden, I believe. Mr. Butler. There was one rather rough senator. Quite profane——"

"Not Mr. Sam Houston, by any chance?"

"That's right—Mr. Houston. From Texas, I believe."

"I believe so," Douglas agreed. "And these gentlemen were all pleased with your anti-slavery clause?"

"No, they didn't like it. However, it wasn't conclusive."

"And so?"

"I'm to see them again."

Douglas waited, but Thornton said nothing further. The "Little Giant" turned severely on Knox Walker.

"Knox, my boy, have you been following this most interesting conversation?"

Walker was horrified. "This is all my fault, Senator. I should have talked to the judge before this. I didn't dream he was dealing with the opposition. I was waiting until you——"

Douglas nodded. "And in the meantime, our friends in the South——"

"I know, sir. I understand. Judge Thornton, may I see you at your lodgings later this afternoon?"

Thornton eyed him with a touch of chill surprise. "I'll be honored, Mr. Walker."

The judge's humble lodgings—almost barren of furniture but scrupulously neat—were some distance from the Capitol. Knox Walker called on him there and explained that the administration was eager to give the settlers everything they wanted—and particularly the anti-slavery clause. In fact, the administration was prepared to wage a finish fight on this point. The settlers out in Oregon must be permitted to make their own choice as to whether Oregon would be slave or free; and Calhoun and his rebels could make the most of it.

The judge didn't seem greatly surprised or impressed. He merely nodded and thanked Walker with gloomy courtesy. The youthful secretary hurried on:

"We'll announce this tomorrow. So it won't be necessary for you to confer any further with Calhoun and his crowd."

"Why not? They've all got votes."

"Yes, yes. But they can't offer *you* anything." Knox Walker spoke confidentially. "What do you want from the President, Judge?"

"I've got all I could hope for: his support."

Walker smiled. "You want me to lead off, eh? Very well. For example, this trip cost you something. You ought to be reimbursed, eh?"

"I presume it would be quite proper. It's government business."

"Of course. How about ten thousand?"

"That seems quite generous."

"It's a deal—*after* the bill passes. Now, there has to be a Federal judge in the new territory. How about the President naming J. Quinn Thornton?"

"It would be a tremendous honor," Thornton agreed. "Most gratifying."

"Consider it done," Walker said with a wave of the hand. "After the bill passes, of course. *And* it has been demonstrated that you're a friend of the administration."

"I have always supported this administration."

Walker chuckled outright and rose to go. "You timed that exactly right at the conference, Judge. You caught old Douglas flat-footed. You're a good poker player."

"Poker playing," Thornton said, "is the devil's pastime."

"And the devil take the hindmost, eh?" Walker took himself off, chuckling. "Very good! Most amusing!"

On August 12, 1848, the Oregon Bill passed by a narrow margin in both houses. It was a milestone in national history, though only a few of the shrewd thinkers of the day grasped its significance. The creation of the Territory of Oregon was of secondary importance to the slavery issue. Debate over the bill split Congress and the nation—a cleavage, North against South, which was to widen inexorably until closed and sealed by the blood of the Civil War.

Meantime the passage of the Oregon Bill was a triumph for the administration. It was a triumph for Joe Meek, whose arrival with the news of the Whitman massacre rallied support for the bill. Joe was loaded with honors, including the appointment as first United States marshal in the new territory.

And the administration didn't forget Judge Thornton. The judge's influence with Sam Houston, Benton, Crittenden, and other Southern leaders perhaps decided the issue in the Senate. At least he was given credit for the crucial votes.

The day after the bill was signed Knox Walker appeared at Judge Thornton's lodgings. He brought with him a suave, shrewd-eyed, and faultlessly dressed companion.

"Ah, there, Judge! . . . Mr. George Sanders—Mr. J. Quinn Thornton, of Oregon."

"Honored, sir," said Sanders with a British accent.

"At your service, sir," said Thornton stiffly.

"Mr. Sanders," Walker explained, "is also a friend of the administration. I've explained to him that you're likely to be the first Federal judge out in Oregon." He gave Thornton a meaning glance and turned away. "Well, I'll toddle along and let you gentlemen discuss matters of mutual interest. See you later, Thornton."

Left alone, the judge and his visitor discussed the gossip of the day: the Oregon Bill, anti-slavery, international affairs. Both were expressionless of manner. Suddenly the Englishman smiled and shrugged.

"Well, Judge, let's not beat about the bush, eh?"

"I'm at your service, sir," Thornton returned.

Sanders opened the door and peered into the dingy hall. It was empty. He closed the door and crossed to the single window. It looked out upon an empty court. Returning, he drew his chair closer and lowered his voice.

"Officially, Thornton, I'm an observer attached to the British Embassy. I also represent Sir George Simpson of London, the governor of the Hudson's Bay Company."

Thornton merely waited. Sanders went on:

"Now, old chap, we—the Hudson's Bay Company—have considerable property out there in Oregon, as you're aware.

There's Fort Vancouver and our tremendous Puget Sound holdings. You'll agree that the United States should buy the whole lot, now that you're a territory?"

"I presume it would be proper and equitable."

"Right. What's the property worth?"

"I would hesitate to say. It would only be my opinion."

"My dear Thornton, your opinion happens to be quite valuable in Washington at the moment. Which explains why I happen to have seventy-five thousand dollars with me. *In cash.*"

"I would say, in all fairness, that the property is worth much more than seventy-five thousand dollars."

The Englishman beamed. "You *do* have a sense of humor, eh, old chap? Come, let's put our cards on the table. The President has already drawn up the treaty which includes the purchase of the property. All but two members of his Cabinet have approved it—and these two have stated they'll approve it if *you* say the price is fair. That's highly complimentary to you, what?"

"It's appreciated. But I've seen no discussion of this in the papers."

"In the papers? Come, come, Thornton! Naturally it was discussed in executive session. And when it goes quietly to the Senate with the unanimous endorsement of the President and his Cabinet—*and* approved by that sterling citizen, J. Quinn Thornton—the rabbit's in the bag, eh?"

"Perhaps. What price is named in the treaty?"

"Three million dollars."

Thornton shook his head. "That's too much—by ten times. I should say that three hundred thousand should be the top figure."

"Walker told me you were a shrewd trader!" Sanders approved. "But we mustn't be *too* grasping, old chap. This seventy-five thousand dollars has to sweeten the dispositions of a number of people. However, the President would like his Cabinet to be unanimous on the treaty. Their vote rests with you. So your share is twenty-five thousand dollars. Is that satisfactory?"

There was a pause, then Thornton said:

"I'm not sure I understand you, sir."

"What can be more understandable than twenty-five thousand dollars—in cash—for merely assuring two Cabinet members that three million dollars is a fair price for our property out there?"

In Thornton's expressionless eyes, for the first time, a dull glow kindled.

"Mr. Sanders, are you attempting to *bribe* me?"

"My dear Thornton!"

"Furthermore," said the gaunt Oregonian, "are you trying to tell me, by implication, that the President of the United States has a personal interest in this bill?"

"Let's forget the play-acting, sir." Sanders began to be annoyed. "This is business. The Hudson's Bay Company——"

"Mr. Sanders, I'll have to ask you to leave!"

The Englishman stared at him. "I beg your pardon?"

"In other words," Thornton said, rising to his feet and pointing to the door, "get out!"

"Nonsense, sir! This is incredible! Knox Walker assured me——"

"I mean now, Sanders! Before I kick you downstairs and into the street!"

"Very well, my friend!" Sanders's face was livid. "You'll hear of this, however. You'll sweat for it, I promise you!"

After Sanders was gone the judge sat down grimly and wrote a letter to President Polk telling what had happened. It was a painful duty, he wrote, but a necessity. The President and Congress should know of this skulduggery. The President, of course, was far above such a design to loot the United States Treasury.

He mailed the letter, and the next day Knox Walker trotted

up the stairs like an indignant terrier. He had the letter in his hand.

"Really, Thornton, you can't send anything like this to the President!"

"Where did you get it?"

"I open the President's mail. It's one of my duties. But you can't put things like this in writing! It just isn't done. You'll have to withdraw it."

"No, I want him to see it," Thornton said. "Kindly hand it to him without fail."

Walker stared at him, his astonishment quickly changing to anger. "What are you up to, Thornton? What's your game? You're not a Federal judge out in Oregon yet, you know."

"That has no bearing. I'm doing my duty."

"Bah! And it'll be your duty to tell Calhoun about this, I suppose? Or give it to the papers?"

"No. It's for the President's private information."

"You insist?" Walker demanded incredulously. "Very well. Good day, sir!"

Several days later a tempest of scandal burst over Washington. The New York *Herald*—most influential newspaper of the era—published a complete account of the attempt to bribe Thornton.

Knox Walker was almost apoplectic. He met the judge on the street and waved a copy of the *Herald* in his face.

"Well, Thornton, what's the meaning of this?"

"I was wondering about it," Thornton admitted. "I didn't tell a soul."

"Nonsense, sir! Only you and I and Sanders knew about it. Would Sanders talk about it?"

"Did *you?*"

"Certainly not! . . . Wait—I did tell Uncle Joe. Joe Meek. But in strictest confidence."

"Joe Meek?" Scorn briefly touched the judge's craglike face. "I think that explains it, Mr. Walker."

He was right. Joe Meek had taken half of Washington into his confidence—including the correspondent of the New York *Herald*. The story effectively killed the treaty. It was withdrawn from the Senate and was not again presented until twenty-two years later.

When final settlement was made with the Hudson's Bay Company after the Civil War, Thornton's judgment was vindicated. The Hudson's Bay property had doubled in value during that twenty-two years. The purchase price agreed upon by a joint commission was not $3,000,000, but $650,000.

Meantime, in Washington, Judge Thornton was in a dilemma. He was ready to return to Oregon and needed the money promised him by the President through Knox Walker. His appeals to the President went unanswered. He found he couldn't even gain an audience with Knox Walker.

One day, however, he was accompanied by a gentleman to whom all official doors in Washington were open—Stephen A. Douglas of Illinois. They reached Walker's desk without difficulty.

"Ah, there, Senator!" Knox greeted him. "Can I be of service?"

"I have with me," Douglas said, "a gentleman from Oregon. His face is familiar?"

"Mr. Thornton is no longer listed among the friends of the administration."

Douglas smiled up at Thornton. "We have short memories here, eh, Judge?"

"I have no complaint, sir."

"And I must tell you, Senator," Walker went on coldly, "that the President no longer has Thornton in mind for the Federal Court in Oregon."

"He could change his mind," Douglas mused. "Shall I make a point of it, Thornton?"

"No, sir. If the President doesn't feel that I'm qualified, the matter is ended."

"Just what *does* the gentleman want?" Walker inquired.

"His wants are few, my boy—just an elemental thing called justice. Mr. Thornton's a poor man. The President agreed to approve an expense item for him, I believe?"

Walker nodded. "If he'll prepare a requisition in triplicate, have it notarized, and present it through the proper channels——"

"Oh no, Knox!" Douglas interrupted. "No. . . . Mr. Thornton would be old and infirm and a new forest would have grown up out there in Oregon before *that* routine had unwound itself. Have a War Department voucher over to his lodgings within the hour, eh?"

"Impossible, Senator! The President's far too busy——"

"Otherwise, Knox, I shall invite Mr. Thornton to stay on in Washington at my expense. And we'll have a full-dress investigation of the Hudson's Bay affair. Is that agreeable?"

"My dear Senator! On second thought——"

"We do have second thoughts here, Thornton," Douglas whispered.

"Very well, Senator. The voucher will be there within the hour."

"Good. Is that satisfactory, Thornton?"

"Yes. And I'm greatly obliged to you, sir."

"It has been a pleasure, Judge," Douglas said affably. "Remember me to those good folks out in Oregon. Someday, you know, Illinois *may* have a candidate for the presidency."

There was a pause, then Thornton said: "And now I will say good-by, Senator. I would like to shake your hand."

"Delighted, of course," Douglas assured him. "Knox, my boy, the gentleman from Oregon is leaving."

"Ah, yes. . . . Good-by, Thornton."

So J. Quinn Thornton walked from the office—and from the Washington scene—without a backward glance. After he was gone Douglas and Knox Walker eyed each other for a moment in silence. Then the "Little Giant" smiled.

"Didn't I tell you, my boy, to beware of these simple, pious men?"

"He was too deep for me," Walker admitted. "He puzzled me completely."

"He would, Knox. I don't mean to embarrass you, my boy, but you *must* learn to deal with men of Thornton's type. Yes, the President must learn too. We do have a few men like Thornton—even in Washington."

"What *is* his type?"

"Can't you guess? He's an honest man, Knox!"

"You mean," Knox said incredulously, "that pious business wasn't a pose?"

"Look at the record, sir. Did he deviate in any particular from his duty as he saw it? . . . Thornton could be a really great man if he had a sense of humor. You know, except that he lacks humor, he reminds me of one of our backwoods congressmen from Illinois."

"Which congressman?"

"That man Lincoln. 'Honest Abe,' they call him out in Springfield." Douglas sighed. "I tell you, Knox, these honest men are dangerous!"

1844 – 1852

In its essence the exploration and development of the last continental frontier—the Oregon Country—followed the pattern of a military campaign, though the conquering settlers were peaceful in intent and their tactics spontaneous and unorganized.

Men like Jedediah Smith, Ewing Young, and Nathaniel Wyeth led the scouting parties which spied out the terrain. The first army to arrive in force was the Great Migration of '43. Reserves poured into the front lines with each succeeding wagon train until the position was secure. Establishment of the Provisional Government in 1843 and of the territorial status in 1848 were formal gestures of victory.

Then came internal expansion, the consolidation of gains. On the heels of the conquerors came the builders. They, too, like the trail blazers, were men of independence and bold imagination. They asked no public favor or subsidy. Unaided and unrestricted, they created their own economy, defended their own security, and left behind them the foundations of today's vast industry, agriculture, and animal husbandry.

Typical of such builders was a quiet, cheerful, indomitable youth named Joseph Watt.

XIV

JOSEPH WATT

YOUNG Joe Watt was an unimpressive and unnoticed figure as he stood shivering on the riverbank at The Dalles that cold evening in late fall of 1844. He was thin, ragged, and barefoot, his freckled face pinched with starvation. He had accompanied a wagon train across the plains, earning his keep by tending the cattle. The train had halted to rest at Grande Ronde, and Joe had hurried on ahead, hoping to work for his passage down the Columbia gorge.

It had been a long haul from Grande Ronde. Food supplies and tempers had been short in the wagon train, and Joe had started out with little food. His shoes had long since worn out. He had walked barefoot through the snow of the Blue Mountains. His feet were bleeding now and blue with cold.

Desperation was in the air here at The Dalles. Winter was close, and the emigrants were building rafts like madmen, loading them and shoving off on the ominous current. Only fifty miles separated them from the valley at this point, but the trip through the gorge, via raft, was the most hazardous in the entire length of the overland trail.

Each family was intent on its own survival. Joe had asked a dozen men for a lift down-river, with no luck. Now it was growing dark, and the last raft of the day was starting out. It was heavily loaded, drifting slowly along the shore. A bearded giant and two of his half-grown sons managed the poles while a woman held smaller children together in the comparative safety of the wagon bed.

Joe limped along the shore and hailed this somber and worried raftsman. He tried to make his voice sound cheerful.

"Hey, mister!"

"Yeah? What d'ye want, bub?"

"Can you take me aboard? I'd like to work my way down to the valley."

"Work?" The man laughed sardonically. "You're worse off than my worn-out oxen back there! Where are your folks?"

"Back in Ohio. They're coming out later if the country looks good. How about it? I could help with the raft on the way down."

"No, you'd just be in the way! I've got troubles enough already!"

Joe leaned against the bank and watched the raft move on. He couldn't have stood without support: his knees were shaking, and not altogether from the cold. He was literally starving and he knew he would never last through another night. The man on the raft was right: he was too weak to be of help. He would never make it to the valley now.

Yet Joe had a theory to which he had always clung. When things look darkest, run a bluff. If you *must* lose, lose cheerfully. Never allow life—or death—to see you beaten and cringing. He was sure in his heart that his theory had failed in the final pinch; yet he leaned against the lonely rocks, head back, his hands in his pockets, whistling. *Oh! Susanna, don't you cry for me . . .*

The man on the raft heard it, looked back through the deepening twilight, and saw him leaning there.

"Doggone it!" he muttered. "He ain't my young one. He'd eat our victuals. Let someone else take him aboard!"

"Let him come, Paw," the woman urged. "There's room. His mother would thank us for it."

"Why didn't his maw keep him to home? Who's looking out for us? Oh, all right!" The man raised his voice gruffly. "Hey, bub! You ain't good for anything else, but can you sing?"

"Sing? Sure I can sing."

"All right, get down here and get aboard. I'll swing in close. . . . We'll put him up front and make him sing for his supper. Maybe the cheerful critter will bring us luck."

So Joe crept aboard and took his place at the forward end of the mountainous craft. His duties were to watch out for rocks—and sing. He was more than ordinarily good at both. By the time they got to the Cascades he was strong enough to help at the portage. When they reached Oregon City he had gained a lifelong friend.

"You're all right, bub," his benefactor told him. "Where do you go from here?"

"Oh, I'll find some work. I want to look the country over. Man, what a valley!"

"When you get ready to settle down, take land alongside us. Whenever I feel plumb discouraged I'll just yell for Joe Watt! Doggone, I wish I had your knack for whittling things down to the proper size!"

That was Joe Watt's outstanding trait—he had a way of making hard luck seem trivial. His freckled face was always cheerful. Difficulties seemed to fade from his path when he sauntered up, his hands in his pockets, whistling. He was soon well known in the valley. "Maybe it isn't as bad as it looks," they'd say jokingly. "Let's send for Joe Watt!"

By the spring of '47 Joe Watt decided he had saved enough capital to return to Ohio for his family. He also mentioned a plan which sounded like sheer folly to older, trail-wise men. With him, across the plains from Ohio, he proposed to bring a band of four hundred sheep! Not scrub sheep, but good stock of the best breed: American Merinos.

He made it sound simple enough. He had to get his family,

anyway, so why not bring the sheep along? The valley needed them. All the old-timers shook their heads. Even Joe's old friend of the Columbia gorge rode around to try to argue him out of the notion.

"I know, Joe—you're lucky and all that. But you can't bring four *hundred* sheep across the plains!"

Joe grinned. "How did your sheep get here?"

"Oh, a wagon outfit can bring along a dozen or so. But you can't carry water in a bucket for four hundred of the half-wits. And you not only got to find water holes—you got to find grass. They've got to be watched day and night. You'll come so slow that no wagon train will wait up for you."

"We'll manage all right," Joe said. "There'll be a big family of us—Mother and Dad and the seven girls."

"Seven *girls?* What'll they amount to in the Indian country?"

"They're mighty dependable—even the little ones. That Roxy, for instance—there's a girl for you! Why, she must be going on twelve by now!"

"Going on twelve! Those mangy Sioux will scalp the lot of you and eat those sheep like squirrels. And what about crossing the Green and the Snake? What about——" The settler shrugged. "All right, Joe. All *right.* I'll be seeing you—maybe. And if so—when?"

"Oh, around the middle of September next year. We'll get an early start, so we'll have good grass all the way."

So Joe Watt set off cheerfully for Ohio. His family helped him buy the sheep that winter and assemble them at St. Joseph, Missouri. They were all American Merinos—435 of them. No such band had ever moved across the plains.

They made their start early in 1848, ahead of the main army of emigrants. All of Joe's capital was invested in the two well-equipped wagons, the ten yoke of good oxen, and the 435 sheep. All those dear to him were gambling their lives on the venture.

184

As the little cavalcade faded into the mighty western horizon, with Joe in the lead and the little girls trudging behind the sheep, more than one seasoned frontiersman at St. Joseph shook his head pityingly. They acted as though they were going on a picnic, but wait till they came to the third crossing of the Platte! Wait till they met up with the Sioux!

In spite of his casual manner, Joe had planned the trip carefully. In his planning, as always, he allowed for a little luck. And luck was with him. The plains warmed up fast that spring. The grass was good. Joe split the sheep into three bands, in charge of the little girls, and they traveled fast. There were no storms on the Platte. The water was low at the dreaded third crossing, and they passed it safely. Each night in camp was fun.

It *was* a prolonged picnic. Long afterward, when the "little girls" were grandmothers, they referred to the haul across the plains as the most delightful experience of their lives.

Then they came to the hunting grounds of the mighty Sioux. It was Joe's turn to guard the sheep that night, and little Roxy, aged twelve, helped to get them settled in the moonlight. Joe was fond of all his sisters, but Roxy was his favorite. She wore a blue gingham dress and her hair in pigtails and was healthy as clover.

After Joe had taken his place on a high point overlooking the sheep and the wagons and stood there leaning on his rifle, Roxy was in no hurry to leave.

"Well, Miss Bopeep," Joe told her, "you'd better get some sleep. I'll look after the sheep."

"Hm-m—poetry!" Roxy said. "Joe, when are we going to see some Indians? You *said* we would."

"Pretty soon now," Joe said gravely. "Remember all that dust we kicked up today? *They've* seen it. . . . But don't be afraid, Roxy."

"I'm not afraid! Will they come tonight?"

"Probably not. Tomorrow, maybe, or the next day."

"Will they have feathers in their hair?"

"I hope not! Nor paint on their faces. That would mean they were on the warpath."

"Why should they be on the warpath?" Roxy asked. "If we're kind to them, won't they be kind to us?"

Joe smiled. "I hope that occurs to them. It's a fine idea. We'll see. . . . Well, you'd better run along to bed, honey."

The Sioux came the next day like a thundering herd—a hunting party, two hundred strong. They followed along the line of march, lolling on their war ponies, studying the sheep. They had seen sheep before, but never such a band as this—and they found them amusing.

They were particularly delighted with a chesty, belligerent old ram whom Roxy had named Pontiac, after the great Ottawa chief. They pretended to be afraid of Pontiac, circling him warily and flinching away in alarm. When Roxy smiled at their antics more than one impassive face lighted up with an answering grin. The chief indicated by signs to Roxy that he, too, had children in his tepee—one this big, one this big, and one *this* big.

They rode away, and the next day they were back again—and brought presents for Roxy and the other little girls. Also, by signs, they told Joe where the best grass was to be found ahead and the most accessible water holes.

It was the same way through the Shoshone and Bannock country. In the fourteen hundred miles to Fort Hall they lost a number of sheep through the ordinary hazards of the trail, but not one was stolen by the Indians.

In camp one night Joe teased Roxy about it.

"I'm going to hire you and Pontiac out as guides, Roxy. You and that woolly dim-wit certainly impress the Indians!"

"Pontiac isn't a dim-wit! He's smart, and he's brave too."

"Yeah?"

"You've seen him every time we come to a ford. The others hold back. They're afraid. But he goes right in, and the others follow him."

"Sure, just showing off."

"But he *isn't* showing off! He just tries it when the others are scared. Just like they told you out there in Oregon that you couldn't bring sheep across the plains. But you're doing it, aren't you?"

Joe chuckled. "Me and old Pontiac make a pair, do we?" Then he spoke more gravely. "You're right, honey. Men and sheep *are* a lot alike. There's got to be a few Pontiacs, I guess. And even the Pontiacs have to have a little luck. I hope our luck holds across the Snake."

Joe Watt's luck—and Pontiac—took them over the lower crossing of the Snake, the worst ford in the entire length of the Oregon Trail. Snow was melting in the mountains, and the water was high. They lost twenty-five sheep there, but the bulk of the flock followed Pontiac across the swollen current to the safety of the farther bank.

They made it safely to the Columbia. The Barlow Trail was open, so they drove the wagons and sheep over the summit and down to Oregon City. They arrived on September 20, 1848, well ahead of the emigrant army of that year.

They were soon established on good land down Yamhill way. People came for miles around to see the sheep. Many of the early settlers had never seen Merinos, and they marveled over the softness of the fleece. Joe wasn't ready to sell any of the flock. He considered them foundation stock and already was thinking in terms of thousands.

That winter hard luck knocked at Joe Watt's door. In the most severe storm in the memory of the white men, one hundred of Joe's precious flock were lost. His old friend of the gorge—a near neighbor now—came over to sympathize with him. He found Joe cheerful as usual. In one wing of the house all the women of the family were busily spinning.

"I was sorry to hear about all those fine sheep you lost, Joe. . . . Doggone! Where did all this fine wool come from?"

"From the dead sheep. Isn't it pretty?"

"I've never seen the beat of it! What's that machine Roxy's working on?"

"It's a carding machine," Roxy told him proudly. "It combs out the wool as fast as anything! I'd rather run the spinning wheel, though. It's my turn tomorrow."

"But, Joe," the settler said doubtfully, "what are you going to do with all the yarn you get out of this?"

"We're knitting socks," Joe said. He took up a pair. "Here's some Mother finished last night."

"Socks? You'll have enough for an army. What'll you do with—— Great snares and bear traps—just feel of that!"

Joe smiled. "It's Merino wool. Soft, isn't it?"

"What have I been wearing all my life? Joe—I'll give you five dollars for this pair! I'll give you six dollars!"

"No," Joe said. "The price other folks will have to pay is three and a half. This pair's yours. And here's three more to go with them. They don't cost you anything."

"And the wool came from a good sheep," Roxy said. "His name was Pontiac."

"I can't do this!" the settler protested. "How come you're *giving* me these socks? After your maw spent so much time on them?"

"Mother insisted on it," Joe said. "It seems she remembered there was a barefoot boy standing on the bank once upon a time up there at The Dalles. He was starving. He was cold. And one of those rough, short-tempered emigrants, who had a raft that was already loaded down——"

"Sho!" the settler protested. "That was over and done with years ago. But don't think for a minute that I ain't keeping these socks!"

"There's a string to it," Joe said. He lowered his voice.

"I've got an idea that I haven't even mentioned to the folks yet. I've had it for a long time."

"I'm for it! What is it?"

"It'll cost you five hundred dollars."

"Five—*what*? I'm agin it!"

"Listen," Joe warned, chuckling. "It's an investment. It'll take some time to get it organized—years, maybe—but I'll do it! I'm going to start a woolen mill."

"A *woolen* mill! Here in the valley?"

"That's right. The first one west of the Mississippi."

"You ain't serious, Joe?"

"Why not?"

"Why, it's a crazy notion! In the first place, where's your machinery? You'll have to ship it around the Horn!"

"Ships sail around the Horn."

"In the second place, after you've built your mill, where will you sell your goods?"

"There's five thousand people in the valley," Joe said. "Ten years from now there'll be thirty thousand."

"But you can't—doggone it, you can't——What's that you're whistling, you freckle-faced——"

Joe went on whistling softly, leaning against the wall, his eyes twinkling a little. In just that manner he had leaned against the darkening rocks at The Dalles four years before. *Oh! Susanna, don't you cry for me* . . .

"You're right, Joe," the settler said gravely. "You'll build your mill. Put me at the head of the list. But five hundred ain't enough. I had a good wheat crop this year. Make it a thousand."

Joe Watt built his mill. It took years, but he didn't give up. The settlers weren't enthusiastic at first. In the end communities were bidding against each other to obtain the plant. Salem won and became the home of the Willamette Valley Woolen Mill—the first west of the Mississippi.

The opening ceremonies were culminated by a grand ball attended by the leading citizens of the valley, including the governor and other state officials. Joe Watt's mother and sisters—including a charming young lady known to her friends as Roxy—walked proudly behind the governor and his lady in the grand march. Again and again during the evening, honoring Joe Watt, the orchestra played "Oh! Susanna."

It was a small mill, but from it grew today's vast industry. Some of the nation's largest bands of sheep now graze in the Columbia basin. Many are descendants of Joe Watt's Merinos. Huge mills now operate in Salem, Brownsville, Oregon City, Pendleton, and Portland, Oregon, and in nearby Washougal, Washington. Portland boasts the largest worsted mill west of the Mississippi, the world's largest manufacturer of knitted swimming suits, and is a national wool market second only to Boston.

These are mighty monuments to that day when young Joe Watt, in late fall of 1844, emerged barefoot from the Blue Mountains, leaving crimson-stained but indomitable footsteps in the drifted snow.

1845 – 1854

One of many mistaken notions about the frontier West is that it was exclusively a "young man's country," that only men and women at the peak of their strength could survive the hardships of overland travel or hope to battle successfully with the wilderness waiting at the end of the trail.

Actually, many a grandmother went along with the wagons. Many a rickety old Missourian got up from his chimney corner, took his squirrel rifle down from the wall, and walked two thousand miles in the choking dust that rolled behind the "cow column." Out in the Oregon Country these oldsters took their part as hewers of wood and drivers of oxen. Many of their names live on today. A few left imperishable works behind them.

One of these was a little, crippled, tireless old grandmother named Tabitha Brown.

XV

IRON WOMAN

IN 1843, a middle-aged, slow-moving, slow-thinking Missourian, Orus Brown, went out to Oregon to look over the country. He was back in Missouri in 1845, tremendously enthused about the Willamette Valley. Early the next spring he began to organize a wagon train.

There were soon forty families committed to go, including Orus and his wife and eight children, and his sister and her husband—the Pringles—with their five children. One day when all plans were completed Orrie dropped in to visit with his mother.

She was sitting in a rocker, knitting: a frail, quiet-mannered little woman with a lace cap framing her bony, placid face. Tabitha Brown always wore a lace cap except in the schoolroom. At home she always wore a neat apron and was always busy. Her heavy cane leaned against the rocker. She had been partially crippled since childhood, but nobody ever heard Tabitha mention her infirmity. A widow for thirty years past, she had supported her family by teaching school. At sixty-six she was still teaching, running her household, and supporting Uncle Brown.

Uncle John Brown was an old sea captain, eleven years older than Tabitha but convinced that he was still young and rugged. He was there with Tabitha, looking shaggy and fierce, smoking his clay pipe. Orrie nodded to them both, seated himself heavily, and stretched his legs.

"Well, Maw, it looks like we'll be pulling out in another three weeks. Too bad you folks can't go along."

"Who says we can't?" Uncle John demanded. "Where'd you young squirts get the notion——"

"Wait, John," Tabitha said. "Orrie, I think I'll resign from school at the end of the term. That'll be about three weeks from now."

"Good! You've got money laid by. It's time you quit and took it easy."

"What I meant was, Orrie—I think John and I will go out West with you."

"To Oregon? Oh no!" Orrie laughed. "You've no idea what crossing the plains is like. Oregon's no place for old folks."

"Old folks!" Uncle John snorted. "Why, you young pup, I can wrassle you right now! Get up from there!"

"Now, wait," Tabitha advised smilingly. "Don't you wrestle Orrie, John. He'll need all his strength."

Orrie stared at her. "Maw, you haven't *decided* on this?"

"I'm afraid so, Orrie. But don't look so alarmed, my dear. We'll have our own wagon. We'll try not to be any bother."

"But who'll drive your wagon? What do you and Uncle John know about oxen?"

"We'll hire a driver. I've already got a good, dependable lad picked out."

"I'll ride a horse!" Uncle John puffed complacently on his pipe. "There's nothing like a life in the saddle! More than once when I was out to sea I says to myself, says I: 'Cap'n Brown——'"

"I know," Orrie cut in. "But, Maw, what'll you *do* out in Oregon?"

"The same as if I'd stayed in Missouri. At my age it's just a habit, I guess." Tabitha Brown laughed. "I'll just keep busy, Orrie."

Tabitha and Uncle John weren't any bother when the train got under way. Uncle John proved a durable man in the saddle: he rode his horse fourteen hundred miles. Tabitha's wagon was the envy of the train. It had a carpet in it and her comfortable rocker.

In night camp she'd sit there, knitting, and folks would somehow gather around her—the tired ones, the lonely ones, and those who were afraid. She didn't talk much, but there was something about Tabitha, sitting there in her lace cap and neat apron, knitting. Missouri didn't seem so far away, somehow. The plains didn't look so big and lonely.

They came finally to Fort Hall. Orrie and the other leading wagons were already past the fort when a plausible settler from Oregon appeared with some wonderful news. At least it *sounded* wonderful. The settler said he'd blazed a new trail to Oregon—an easier trail which swung to the south of the high desert and around the Cascades. It avoided the Columbia gorge. It was shorter, faster, with good grass along the way. It wouldn't cost much—just a moderate tax on each wagon for guide services.

The men of the train—and of following trains that overhauled them while they debated—voted to take this new and pleasant detour. Uncle John voted with them. The women had no vote, but that night as she and Uncle John discussed the plan Tabitha was dubious.

"I don't know, John. I've a feeling we ought to follow along after Orrie on the regular trail."

"Oh no, we'll beat him to the valley. That'll teach the young swab a thing or two!"

"But this man was a little too plausible," Tabitha said. "He was riding a horse. No wagons have actually traveled this new route."

"What of it? Ten years ago no wagons had gone over *this* trail!"

Tabitha sighed. "I'm not worried about myself. It's Fern and her children and all those others. And you're not very strong."

"What?" Uncle John shouted.

"I'm just selfish, I suppose," Tabitha said. "I don't mind losing the wagon, but will I ever find another rocking chair as comfortable as this one out there in Oregon?"

Tabitha was right. Survivors of the train never forgot their sufferings over the "easier, shorter" route. There was no trail. They lost their cattle in waterless deserts hundreds of miles to the south. Hostile Indians clung to their flanks like vultures, stealing their horses and shooting their oxen with poisoned arrows. In early winter, in the forested and trackless wilds of southern Oregon, their guide abandoned them.

The controversy over who was responsible for the hardships and deaths on the detour raged for a generation in the valley. None of the accounts of the trip are more vivid than those written by Tabitha herself. Her wagon—and her comfortable rocker—were lost on the Rogue River. She and Uncle John had nothing left but the horses they rode. They traveled with her daughter's family, the Pringles; and of the terrible twelve-mile battle to the Umpqua Valley Tabitha wrote simply:

Out of the hundreds of wagons, only one came through without breaking. The canyon was strewn with dead cattle, broken wagons, beds, clothing, and everything but provisions—of which we were nearly all destitute. Some people were in the canyon two or three weeks before they could get through. Some died without warning, from fatigue and starvation. Others ate the flesh of cattle that were lying dead by the wayside.

In the Umpqua Valley there were still timbered mountains ahead, whitened with snow. It was now early in December, and winter had set in. The Pringles, near starvation, insisted that Tabitha and Uncle John should go on alone and try to overhaul three wagons that were far in the lead. So Tabitha divided the last of her bacon with her daughter's family— keeping three slices of bacon for herself and Uncle John— and they started out.

They rode northward alone into the West's most rugged wilderness, through dripping forests. They were unarmed, starving, bowed under lashing rain and snow. Uncle John was no longer a dashing figure even in his own imagination; he was a doddering and helpless old man, his strength failing fast. Tabitha was as calm as ever. In her account of the second day and night there was no criticism of Uncle John. She even tried to give him dignity by referring to him as Captain Brown:

In the afternoon Captain Brown complained of sickness and could only walk his horse at a short distance behind. He had a swimming in his head and pain in his stomach. In two or three hours he became delirious and fell from his horse.

This was a development that had terrifying aspects. Tabitha, crippled, was unable to mount her horse without help. If she dismounted to help Uncle John, she herself would be afoot. Nevertheless, she found a way out of her desperate dilemma:

I rode close to him and set the end of his cane—which I held in my hand—hard in the ground to help him up. I then urged him to walk a little. He tottered along a few yards and then gave out. I then saw a sunken spot in the ground a few yards away and led his horse to it, and with much difficulty got him raised to the saddle. I then told him to hold fast to the horse's mane and I would lead by the bridle.

Night overtook them at the base of a timbered ridge. The rain and sleet had stopped, but a cold wind moaned through the forest. They could no longer see wagon tracks ahead, so Tabitha got off her horse—knowing she might never be able to mount again—and took off the saddle. Under the saddle was a folded canvas which she shook out and placed over a limb, forming a small tent. Into that shelter she dragged all her equipment—and Uncle John, who had completely collapsed. She piled all their blankets over him and sat down at his feet, expecting to die in the night.

Of those black hours she wrote calmly:

Wolves were fighting and howling all around me. Dark clouds hid the stars. But that kind Providence I had always known was watching over me still. I committed all to Him and felt no fear. As soon as the light dawned I pulled down my tent, saddled my horse, and found that the captain was able to stand on his feet. Just at that moment one of the emigrants I was trying to over-take came up. He was in search of venison. Half a mile ahead were the wagons we were trying to locate. We were soon there and ate plentifully of fresh meat.

Tabitha's Providence continued to watch over her. A few days later, when they were struggling northward through the deepening snow, still far from the valley, Orrie Brown appeared with a pack train of provisions. Orrie and the others who had stayed on the regular trail beyond Fort Hall had been safe in the valley for two months past, but news of the desperate plight of the emigrants to the south had just reached the settlement.

It was still a bitter struggle northward, but they finally made it to the upper Willamette River. There Tabitha traded the horses for transportation down-river, and at long last they reached Salem, in the heart of the valley. The settlers opened their homes to the ragged, half-starved, half-dead survivors. Some of those who had been young and strong at Fort Hall had to be carried across the threshold, but Tabitha Brown walked unaided into the home of a Methodist minister, a bundle of clothing under her arm, leaning on her cane.

That night was the first time she had slept under a roof in nine months. She had lost her life savings. All she owned was that bundle of clothing. But she slept soundly. The next day she was up and around, helping with the housework.

Several days later Orrie came from the Tualatin Plains, where his land was located. He discussed her future gloomily.

"I dunno, Maw. Until I can build a cabin, I don't know what we're going to do with you and Uncle John. And the Pringles ain't located yet."

"Now, Orrie," Tabitha reproved, "that isn't very complimentary. *We'll* get along."

"But how?"

"I've already arranged to work here for my board and Uncle John's. They like my cooking. I *can* cook—remember?"

"Oh, sure, but they can't pay any wages. And you're not as young as you were, you know." Orrie sighed. "Back in Missouri, where you had your own home——"

"Listen, Orrie," Tabitha said confidentially. "I brought some money with me. I didn't know it, but I found it tucked away in an old glove. Wasn't that lucky?"

"Good!" Orrie said, relieved. "That's better."

"Now you go back and don't worry about me. I'll be up to visit you one of these days. And I'll take good care of Uncle John. You know, Orrie, he isn't very strong."

Tabitha hadn't told Orrie how much money she had found in the old glove. It was one small coin—what they called a "picayune" back in old Missouri. It was worth exactly six and a quarter cents.

With that coin Tabitha Brown, age sixty-seven, began her career in a "young man's country."

She bought three needles with the six and a quarter cents. She had one extra dress in her bundle, and she traded that dress to an Indian woman for some beautiful buckskin. From the buckskin she made gloves during the winter, which she sold for thirty dollars.

She now found a place for Uncle John and went with the Methodist minister and his wife down to Astoria. In October of that year—1847—she returned upriver with friends in an open boat. They had to fight wind and current all the way, and it required thirteen days to cover the one hundred and twenty miles back to Oregon City.

Rested and refreshed by this experience—which had exhausted the rest of the party—she went over to the west side of the Tualatin Plains to visit Orrie. There she met the Reverend Harvey Clark, whose claim included the present site of Forest Grove. The Clarks grew fond of her and invited her to stay with them all winter. She did so and kept busy—but not busy enough to satisfy her.

One evening in early spring, when Tabitha was sitting by the fireplace knitting furiously, Reverend Clark paused and looked down at her with a twinkle in his eye.

"What's wrong, Grandma? Every time you knit that fast there's something in the wind. Out with it, now!"

"Harvey, if I were a wealthy woman, do you know what I'd do?"

"What?"

"I'd establish myself in a comfortable home and take in poor children and teach them and be a mother to them."

Clark was impressed. "Why not? There are a lot of orphans hereabouts. There's only one school in the valley—away over there at Salem. . . . Yes, I'll do it! I'll help you get started."

That was the spring of 1848. They established Tabitha in the log meeting house, which was located in a beautiful grove of oak trees on Reverend Clark's property. The settlers helped furnish it. Tabitha used some of her own capital.

By midsummer she had thirty children in her boarding school. For those parents who could pay it, the total charge per child was one dollar a week. This included board, tuition, and washing. Tabitha worked the first year for nothing, but the school grew fast. Trustees were appointed in the spring of '49, and the tuition was raised to two dollars a week.

It was now Tualatin Academy, and the Reverend Clark donated thirty acres to it. By 1851 there were forty students at two dollars and a half a week, and Tabitha was allowed whatever "profit" she could make above costs, which included an assistant teacher. She was an excellent manager.

She fed the children enormous meals. That winter, with her own hands, she mixed and baked into bread 3,423 pounds of flour. She was then seventy-one years old.

Orrie came in to see her in the summer of 1854. He found her sitting on the porch, knitting, her cane leaning against the rocker. Orrie was proud of the business that had brought him.

"Well, Maw, I finally built onto the cabin. You might as well move in with us, now that you've retired."

Tabitha shook her head. "Thank you, Orrie, but I think I'd better stay in town, close to the school. I can still help out."

"But you can't live on charity! I won't stand for that!"

"Thank you, my dear. I'll get along fine. I've got a little money laid by."

"Now, Maw! How could you do that when you've been working right along here at the school?"

"Well, I suppose you're entitled to know," Tabitha said a little unwillingly, "so you won't worry about me. I bought eight cows and some young cattle and rented them out for their milk and half of their increase. Now I own that white house facing the campus. It rents for one hundred dollars a year."

"Yeah?" Orrie said, impressed. "But that ain't enough to live on."

"Well, I've also got eight lots over town. I can sell them for twelve hundred dollars any time, but I'm sure they're going to keep growing in value. Besides, I've got over one thousand dollars loaned out. I hate to charge interest, but I want to leave as much as I can for the school."

"Well, I'll be——!" Orrie laughed. "Maw, you sure beat all! You not only started a school in your spare time, but you make more money than I do farming! Wait—you fetched part of your capital across the plains, didn't you?"

"Mm-m—yes," Tabitha admitted. "Enough to get started

with. Then it kind of grew. That's what I like about this country, Orrie. Get them started right, and things just seem to grow."

The school continued to grow. That fall Tabitha wrote to friends in the East—a letter dated "Forest Grove, Oregon Territory, August 1854"—in which she referred in her usual calm and matter-of-fact way to the subject closest to her heart.

Mr. Clark made over to the trustees the quarter section of land for a town plot. A large and handsome building is on the site we selected at the beginning. It has been under town incorporation for two years, and at the last session of the legislature a charter was granted for a university to be called Pacific University.

That event—the founding of Pacific University—was the crowning milestone in Tabitha Brown's career. She died shortly afterward and was buried at Salem near Uncle John, who had already passed away.

We know that death had no terror for Tabitha Brown. Why should it? She had kept busy. She had done her work well. Now it was time to go. . . . So it was only her bent and outworn body they buried in Salem near Uncle John. Tabitha Brown herself, being made of imperishable ingredients, merely threw her cane away, adjusted her lace cap and smoothed her neat apron, and set out cheerfully upon the longest and most beautiful trail.

1848

By 1848 the Willamette Valley had grown into a large and comfortable community, isolated from the world. There was Indian trouble beyond the mountains, but the valley itself was as peaceful as a vast inland sea. Little money was in circulation, but little was needed. An occasional ship entered the Columbia, but except for the dwindling fur trade and some lumber and wheat shipped to the Sandwich Islands, there were no exports. The land was rich, the climate mild, the people industrious and congenial.

Then in August of that year came an event as sudden and startling as the explosion of a giant bomb. It changed the entire economy of the region, and almost overnight. It brought the thing called "progress"—plus all the benefits and complexities of commerce—and it destroyed the Arcadian simplicity of the valley forever.

That event was the discovery of gold in California. The strike was made by an Oregonian, John Marshall, who had gone south the summer before to work at Sutter's Mill. The news spread to all points of the compass like wildfire. It permeated the valley quickly and disarranged the life pattern of a thousand homes, including that of Jeff Clarke, on the banks of the Tualatin River.

XVI

GOLD!

JEFF CLARKE'S HOMESTEAD lay just over the hills from Oregon City: a comfortable farm on the rich bottom lands bordering the Tualatin River. At near noon of that day in early August 1848, Jeff had saddled his horse and gone over to Oregon City to buy some odds and ends of supplies at Abernathy's store.

It was early evening now. He should be back any minute. Elvie, Jeff's oldest daughter, stood at the cabin door listening. Elvie, aged twelve, was big and healthy. She could turn off as much work, almost, as a grown woman. She was smart, too; she kept her ears open and generally knew what was going on around her. The little children were playing on the split-rail fence, but they weren't making much noise. At that hour in the valley you could hear a horseman coming from a long way off.

Suddenly Elvie began to dance, her pigtails wiggling.

"Here he comes, Maw! I can hear him! He's coming over the hill!"

"Good," her mother said. She was working over the stove, her face flushed a little with the heat. "Call the children in, Elvie. I'll get the things on."

"Joe!" Elvie yelled. "Betty! Come and get washed for supper! Daddy's coming! . . . He's coming awful fast, Maw! He's galloping right through the swale!"

Her mother gave a little gasp of dismay. "No! I wonder . . . ? Oh, I hope he hasn't got another *idea!* That man!"

205

"He's gonna break that jug of molasses, sure as shooting. Whoops—he's over the ditch, all right! His horse is all covered with sweat! What's wrong with having ideas, Maw?"

"Never mind, never mind. Maybe I can talk him out of it." Her mother scanned the table anxiously. "We've got everything he likes to eat tonight—chicken and dumplings, and squash. Yes, I'll put on some of my wild strawberry jam. Oh, I hope his mind isn't made up—whatever it is!"

"But he's laughing, Maw! Look at him—he's feeling fine!"

"I know."

Elvie dashed out to put the horse away. "I'll take him, Daddy! I'll put him away."

Jeff Clarke brought his blowing horse to a stop. He was a big, jovial man. "Gangway, kids! Hi there, Elvie!" His black eyes were fierce with excitement. "Here—grab this jug! Where's Maw?"

"Here, Jeff." His wife came to the door, her hands fumbling in her apron. She whispered: "Oh dear—I suppose I ought to be thankful he doesn't drink or gamble or things like that. But will he *ever* grow up?"

Jeff crossed to her and clapped her on the shoulder. "Well, honey! Listen, have *I* got news! Everybody over at Oregon City's gone crazy over it. They're all heading for California! So am I—tomorrow morning! Me and Anderson and Carrauthers! We'll each take a saddle horse and two pack horses——"

"*Jeff!* Please—don't be so excited. Why go to California?"

"Why go to——" A measure of sanity returned to him. "Gold, that's why! *Gold!*"

"Gold?"

"There's a ship tied up alongside Pettygrove's village down the river—at Portland! The captain's bought all the wheat and potatoes he could lay hands on—and picks and shovels and pans! Bread pans! Wash pans! Any kind of pans! Why, they're scooping the gold out of the sand down there. The hills are full of it. There's *mountains* of it!"

His wife leaned wearily against the doorframe. "Gold. . . . Oh, Jeff! If you take the horses, how'll we get the wheat harvested? And the apple trees are just starting to bear."

"Wheat! Apples!" Jeff threw back his head and laughed. "Why, we'll be *rich!* You'll be wearing silk and satin! We'll take the kids back East to the best schools! Nothing'll be too good for—— Honey, don't you *understand?*"

"I'm afraid so, Jeff. First it was starting a mill. Then you were going to build a ferry. Anything but farming. Now it's gold. . . . We've a *good* farm here, Jeff. Please don't rush into this."

"Sure I'll rush into it! It's first come, first served down there! I got to get started bright and early tomorrow morning." Jeff pushed her almost roughly into the cabin and tossed his hat into the corner. "Now don't you say another word, honey! *This* time I'll make it, sure. . . . What you got there—chicken and dumplings? And squash? Good—that'll stick to my ribs! It'll give me a good start in the morning. . . . What's in this jar?"

"Some wild strawberry jam. I thought maybe you'd like it, Jeff."

Yes, the greatest placer gold strike of all time had been made in California. The news swept the valley like a tornado. Overnight, almost, an estimated three thousand men—practically every able-bodied man in the valley—left for the gold fields. Crops were left standing in the fields. Blacksmiths left their forges. Stores and gristmills closed. Upon the women and children and the old and crippled fell the burden of caring for the livestock, getting in the wood, harvesting enough grain to last through the winter—all the things which had to be done if homes and families were to survive.

That was a bad winter at the Jeff Clarke homestead. Jeff had always been an enthusiast, a dreamer of big dreams.

Beside the cradle over each of their children he and his wife had planned their future. Its promise always lay ahead. Somewhere—over yonder—was the Happy Land. . . . The search had taken them from Ohio to Missouri and across the plains.

And here, this winter night on the banks of the Tualatin, the good ground was covered with snow, the river was frozen, and the icicles hung from the eaves of the cabin like the manes of white horses. This was the winter of '48, the coldest and with the deepest snow in the memory of white men. This was the time when Joe Watt lost his sheep and the McNemee family down in Portland took the straw from their mattresses and fed it to their cow to keep it alive.

In the Jeff Clarke cabin the little children had gone to bed, but Elvie and her mother still sat close to the fireplace, heads bowed, listening to the roaring of the wind in the timber. It was darker than usual that night because the drifts were higher than the east windows.

Elvie spoke suddenly. "Maw, there's tears in your eyes! Are we done for? Are we gonna freeze to death?"

"Oh no," her mother said. "No, dear, we'll get along all right."

"Well, we're almost out of wood."

"I know, but that dead tree fell at the edge of the swale today. We'll bring in a lot of dry limbs and bark tomorrow."

"Well, then, are we gonna starve to death?"

"Of course not. We've still got some of the wheat left that we tramped out last fall. And Mrs. Carrauthers told me before it snowed that she would kill her old ox and divide it with us."

"*I* know what you're worried about!" Elvie boasted. "We haven't got any horse or oxen, so we can't put in any wheat next spring. So we're bound to starve next winter, sure! Is that it?"

"No, dear. Mrs. Anderson's got oxen, but she isn't strong

enough to manage a plow. I can, though, so you and I will plant some wheat for Mrs. Anderson, then we'll plant ours. We'll try to put in twenty acres at least."

"What *is* wrong, then? What are you crying for? I'm old enough to know about things. Tell me about it and I'll— I'll——"

"What will you do?"

"I'll cry too!"

Her mother laughed. "Bless your heart, honey. . . . I wasn't really crying. I was just thinking about your daddy. I hope he isn't sick down there. Or hungry . . ."

Down on the American River, Jeff Clarke was one of frenzied thousands. Some were finding gold—much gold— but others were not. Some had been killed by the Indians. Many had died of fever. Jeff was desperately eager to succeed. He had had many enthusiasms before; this time he *must* make good. The best claims were gone before he and his friends arrived, but they prospected higher in the hills and found a promising sand bar. They worked day and night and finally reached bedrock that was speckled with yellow nuggets and dust.

News of their good luck soon drifted north to the valley. The Oregon army had already begun its homeward march, a few loaded with gold, but many others penniless, ragged, and half starved.

On the Jeff Clarke homestead, one warm spring day, Elvie and her mother were plowing. Elvie was driving the oxen; her mother was clinging to the plow. It was rough, back-breaking work, and when they paused for a moment to rest Elvie spoke disgustedly.

"Maw, what are we plowing for? Dad's rich."

"Maybe so, honey," her mother said, her cheek resting on her arm. "But we're going to get the wheat planted."

"But why? You heard what that man said over at Oregon City. Dad's making a hundred dollars a day at his mine. He's been doing it for sixty days, the man said, so he's already got at least six thousand dollars. So why get yourself all tired out planting wheat?"

"Well, it'll bring a good price. They're going to ship all the wheat they can down to California. . . . You see, dear, something *might* happen to your daddy. He might lose his gold. I can't take any chances—not with you children to feed next winter!"

"My, won't it be fine when Daddy comes riding home with buckets and buckets of gold?"

"Don't, honey. Just hope he comes home safe and sound. Never mind the gold."

For sixty-six days Jeff Clarke washed out one hundred dollars a day on his sand bar. On the sixty-seventh day his four companions were killed by Indians. Clarke escaped, organized a company of Oregon men, and drove the Indians into the hills. When he came back he found his cabin burned down, his gold stolen from its hiding place—and the spring freshet had washed the sand bar away.

His chances now looked hopeless. News of the strike had brought thousands of more men pouring into the gold fields —by wagon train from the East and on ships around the Horn. But Jeff worked for wages and bought a claim from a speculator. It turned out to be good ground, and he soon had options on six adjoining claims.

By midsummer he was employing twenty men. He had paid for his claims, built a flume to carry water to high ground, and had reached bedrock, where the richest sand was concentrated. His first day's operations at bedrock yielded one hundred ounces, or sixteen hundred dollars in nuggets and dust.

Three days later—overworked, staggering with weariness —he was stricken by a raging fever. He tried to get out to the claim but collapsed. His crew were not Oregon men. A different fever was burning in their veins. There was no law yet on the gold creeks. They carried Clarke down to the new town of Sacramento and abandoned him in a river-front shack.

Jeff was delirious, and in his delirium he thought he had come back triumphantly to his homestead on the far-off Tualatin River.

"Well, I made it, honey!" he whispered through parched and burning lips. "Look at it! Heft those nuggets in your hand! It's *gold,* my dear. . . . Seventy-five thousand dollars. Better than a thousand a day for two months. . . ." He couldn't help boasting a little. "You never thought I'd make it, eh? Why, honey, hang that apron on the wall! You'll never do a lick of housework again! The kids'll never work like we have. They'll live in marble halls. . . ." Then he turned weaker. "Elvie, fetch your daddy another drink of water. I dunno why it is—I've drunk a barrel of it—and I'm still thirsty. . . ."

Up on the banks of the Willamette, Elvie and her mother harvested twenty acres of wheat. Elvie and the little ones did the threshing. They put the grain into an enclosure and put the cattle in—particularly the active young heifers. Then Elvie and the others each took hold of a heifer's tail, and around and around they went, the heifers getting more and more excited and the children laughing and shouting.

After the grain was tramped out came the tedious business of tossing the chaff into the air when a stiff breeze was blowing. The wind blew the chaff away, leaving the wheat on the outstretched canvas. Then the wheat had to be sacked, and the neighbors hauled it down to Oregon City. From there it was barged down to Portland and whole shiploads were hurried on to San Francisco, where there wasn't enough wheat —or potatoes, or apples, or anything that could be eaten—to feed the tens of thousands of people rushing into the gold fields.

One evening at near sundown in late September the children were playing down by the creek, out of sight of the cabin. Elvie's mother was setting the table for supper, when Elvie hurried in, excited and breathless.

"Maw—you'd better get the rifle down! There's a tramp coming across the swale!"

"Maybe it's an Indian!" said her mother, alarmed. "I'd better call the children in!"

"No," Elvie said, looking around the corner of the cabin, "he's no Indian—he's got whiskers! But he's awful ragged. Come over and look."

Her mother came cautiously to the corner. "Your eyes are better than mine, Elvie. What's he doing? It looks like he's crawling."

Elvie laughed. "He just fell in the creek. There, he's up again. Look at him stagger along! I'll bet he's drunk."

"No, he's just weak, poor man. See how he walks, with his head hanging. . . . Elvie!" her mother gasped, then her voice rose strongly: "*Jeff!* Oh, Jeff honey—wait, *wait!* I'll help you. . . ."

Yes, it was Jeff Clarke, home from the gold fields as many another Oregonian had come: ragged, stumbling, and alone. When he had recovered from his malaria down in Sacramento and had returned to his claim, he found his helpers had stripped the ground of its last grain of gold. Nobody knew how much they had taken or where they had gone. To hunt for them was useless. His treasure was already lost, scattered to the four winds.

So Jeff Clarke, his spirit broken and his once powerful frame wasted with fever, had exchanged the last of his nuggets for boat passage to Portland. He had staggered home on foot from Oregon City, avoiding his neighbors.

He was still weak, apathetic, as he sprawled on the kitchen

chair and told his adventures. His wife listened, her eyes shining. Elvie, getting the supper on, didn't miss a word.

"I haven't any excuses to make," Jeff concluded, his shaggy head bowed. "I'm just naturally a failure. I had my hands on it—I was *rich*—but it got away from me. And you and the kids practically starving here!"

"Starving?" Elvie said. "I guess you haven't noticed what I'm dishing up. Look—chicken and dumplings! There's squash too. . . . Maw, you knew he was coming, I betche."

"I knew he'd come sooner or later, honey," her mother said. "This is his home."

"I better call the kids! Boy, wait till *they* find out he's back!"

"Wait, Elvie. . . . Before they come, Jeff, I want to tell you something. Are you listening?"

"Yeah," Jeff said with feeble humor. "I'm too weak to run. I've got to listen."

"It's this, my dear," his wife said in a matter-of-fact voice but with her hands twisted in her apron. "What did you go down to California for?"

"Why, I went after gold. And I had it too—had it right in my hands——"

"Wait. . . . There's more gold right here, Jeff, than they'll ever find in California. Right here in the valley."

"Yeah?" Jeff said, rousing at once. "Where'd they find it? Over on Gales Creek? How much is it running to the pan?"

"No, no—listen. We bought eight heifers while you were gone, Jeff. And we've got four cows milking. We've got three good work horses——"

"And chickens and pigs!" Elvie put in. "You didn't see them because they've all gone to roost." She giggled. "The chickens, I mean."

"Well, I'll be——" Jeff peered up at his wife. "Where'd you get all this livestock? Who do you owe for the horses and heifers?"

"Nobody. I paid for them."

"With what?"

"With gold. California gold."

"But doggone it—where did you get the gold?"

"From the wheat we sold. . . . Listen, Jeff. That's the point. Elvie and I put in twenty acres of wheat. We harvested eight hundred bushels. We saved some for flour and seed— and sold the rest for *two dollars and a half* a bushel! They paid for it with gold that just came up from California."

"Two dollars and——" Jeff whistled. "That's right—flour's four bits a pound up on the gold creeks! They got to have flour!"

"Yes—hundreds and hundreds of tons of it! And potatoes and apples and bacon—anything we can raise. Do you know how much seed I saved out? Enough for *eighty* acres. There's eighty acres in the big meadow, all ready to break. . . . Don't you *see*, Jeff?"

"Hm-m," Jeff said, scowling at her. "So you and the kids harvested twenty acres of wheat. . . ."

"Of course. It just grows. It wasn't hard to do."

"Wasn't hard?" Elvie said. "Hah! You should have seen me helping Maw into bed each night!"

"You'll get your strength back, Jeff. We'll soon fatten you up. I know you've got *plenty* of courage."

"Courage?" Jeff said. "If I run out I'll just borrow from you and Elvie!" He looked around him, blinking; and all of a sudden it was as though a bad dream was over and he was home again. "Where are the kids? Why don't we eat instead of setting here talking?"

"You better call them now, Elvie," her mother said.

"Man, look at those dumplings!" Jeff said. "And California'll never raise squash like that! . . . What's in this jar?"

"Some of my wild strawberry jam. I saved it for you, Jeff.

I thought maybe you'd like some when you got back again."

Outside Elvie was yelling as though she didn't care if the whole valley heard it. "Joe! Betty! Come and get washed for supper! *Hurry! Daddy's home!*"

1850

By 1850 it was generally known in shipping circles of the world that the Columbia River would be the next big source of sea-borne traffic. On both sides of the Columbia towered the world's mightiest forest. The California gold fields offered a rich market for the agricultural products of the vast Willamette Valley. Shipping company executives were studying charts of the Columbia bar and marking an "X" on their sketchy maps of the upper river.

"X" represented the as yet undesignated trade center of this vast empire. It could be anywhere along the one hundred and fifteen miles from the mouth of the Columbia to the head of navigation on the Columbia's largest tributary: the Willamette River, which drained the three-million-acre Willamette Valley. Six different communities claimed the honor. The least impressive of the six, a mere frontier village, was a small settlement on the Willamette called Portland.

Yet Portland emerged from fierce competition as the metropolis of the Columbia basin. The choice vindicated the faith of two men—two good gamblers—and demonstrated again that no human agency can resist natural laws as immutable as the flow of great rivers to the sea.

XVII

A CITY IS BORN

EVEN by frontier standards the village of Portland looked raw and primitive in 1850. There seemed to be no excuse for its existence except the enthusiasm of its three promoters, Stephen Coffin, Daniel H. Lownsdale, and W. W. Chapman.

The townsite was carved from the dense forest on the west bank of the Willamette River, ten miles upstream from the Willamette's junction with the Columbia and ninety-two miles from the sea. There were no farm lands near it. Behind the city reared a one-thousand-foot timbered ridge known as Council Crest, on whose highest point the Multnomah Indians had lighted their council fires for centuries before the white man came. A single muddy and almost impassable wagon trail known as the Canyon Road led over this barrier to the Tualatin Plains, the northernmost section of the immense Willamette Valley.

The village boasted a population of three hundred, and people up and down the river wondered how such numbers could support themselves there or what possible promise the future held. All rival communities could claim specific advantages. Oregon City, fifteen miles upriver, was not only the capital of the territory but was located on the falls of the Willamette, which furnished power for gristmills and sawmills. The booming town of Milwaukie, promoted by an enthusiast named Lot Whitcomb, was on the opposite bank of the river upstream from Portland, and therefore enjoyed the business of the incoming wagon trains from the East.

Other down-river communities had similar claims to permanence. Fort Vancouver, on the Columbia itself, former headquarters for the immense trade of the Hudson's Bay, had been established for thirty years past. St. Helens, farther down the broad Columbia, pointed to its adjacent forests and natural deep-water channel. Astoria, at the mouth of the Columbia, was the oldest settlement of all and practically on the ocean itself.

Portland, by contrast, could boast of but two mediocre details. It was the point where sailing ships happened to tie up at the bank because they could get no farther up the Willamette River. And it was joined to the Willamette Valley by the Canyon Road, rutted in summer and a quagmire in winter—unquestionably the worst four-mile stretch of "road" west of the Mississippi.

Nevertheless, on a summer day in 1850, there was plenty of activity at the Portland townsite. At the point where the Canyon Road reached the river there were a half dozen stores and a blacksmith shop. New cabins were going up in the shadow of the two-hundred-foot wall of forest. South of the clearing a crew of men were struggling with some huge hand-hewn timbers obviously designed as the foundation for some substantial manufacturing plant.

Watching the crew was jovial Steve Coffin, one of the townsite promoters. He was in his shirt sleeves and was about to give the perspiring workmen a hand with the timbers when he saw one of his partners approaching. It was Lownsdale: tall, handsome, well dressed. Lownsdale had just returned from an important conference with shipping executives at Astoria.

"Well, Dan!" Coffin greeted him. "Ain't you an elegant picture!" They carried on a pretended feud on this point, though Coffin was secretly proud of his partner's fashionable appearance. "May I talk to you, *Mister* Lownsdale?"

"You may," Lownsdale said. "But with respect, my good

man." He drew off his gloves, frowning. "What's all this, Steve? Has Abrams decided to go ahead with the steam saw-mill, after all?"

"Oh, sure. I told him we'd back him up."

"So? When did *we* agree to back him up?"

"Why, last spring! Didn't you and Chapman agree that we had to help the farmers fix the road up the blasted canyon? Well, it's got to be planked. The mud's axle-deep. To cut planks you've got to have a mill."

Lownsdale smiled. "You're a stubborn soul, Steve! What good will it do the farmers to bring wheat here before there's ships to haul it away?"

"And why bring ships here until we've got cargo for them? . . . All right—let's hear your end of it. How did you get along with those pirates down at Astoria? Is the Pacific Mail going to fetch their steamboats up here?"

"Unfortunately, no. They're talking about moving their terminus upriver, but they seem to have St. Helens firmly in mind."

Coffin grew excited at once. "Now there you are! St. Helens is building a road over to Tuality Plains, ain't they? We've already got a road—if we ever get it planked! . . . Just hang that beautiful hat on a limb, Mr. Lownsdale. We'll give these boys a hand."

Lownsdale did so, sighing. "How big is this mill going to be?"

"You'd never believe it. It'll cut ten thousand feet a day!"

"My word! They can't say we aren't optimists, Steve!"

Yes, that was an enormous mill in those days. Even Steve Coffin didn't dream that three quarters of a century later Portland would be the world's leading lumber manufactur-ing city, its mills capable of cutting ten thousand board feet each three working *minutes*. In 1850 the idea of a mill of such size on the Willamette was fantastic.

It caused many a chuckle up and down the river. Up at

Oregon City and at Milwaukie—and particularly down at St. Helens—they waited confidently for those Portland enthusiasts to go broke. Bets were laid that the mill would never be built. But when the plant actually began to take form, Lot Whitcomb, Milwaukie's promoter, decided the time had come to eliminate this upstart village from public notice.

Lownsdale brought the bad news back from Oregon City, where the third Portland townsite partner, Chapman, had his office. Chapman, a lawyer, was kept busy clearing title to townsite lots and had heard of the big events over at Milwaukie.

"It looks bad, Steve," Lownsdale reported. "Whitcomb's putting in *two* steam sawmills over at Milwaukie."

Coffin refused to be impressed. "What's bad about that? Let him put in twenty mills. Ours will be running first—and we'll be turning out planks for the road."

"He's also putting in a free ferry across the river."

"Good! Why didn't we think of that? We'll put one in too. It'll bring more emigrants this way."

"But listen to this—Whitcomb's building a river boat. He's going to set up regular service between Milwaukie and Astoria—to connect with the Pacific Mail!"

"*That*," Steve Coffin asserted, "is just plain talk."

"But Chap says he's already got the engine. And he's brought an engineer named Jacob Kamm up from San Francisco to install it."

"Hm-m. Maybe Whitcomb isn't bluffing, at that. . . . All right, let him build it! Where's he going to get his cargo? Meantime, doggone it, we'll get that road planked over the hill!"

Lot Whitcomb wasn't bluffing. He built the river boat and launched it Christmas Day, 1850. He named it the *Lot Whitcomb*. And shortly afterward, with flags flying and smoke pouring from her funnel, she went proudly down-river on her first run to Astoria. She plowed past Portland as though that riverbank community didn't exist, disdaining even to blow her whistle to the watchers on the bank.

A worse blow followed. Two weeks later the Pacific Mail moved upriver and established its terminus at St. Helens. It announced that the *Lot Whitcomb* and its own river boat, the *Columbia*, would handle all Willamette Valley traffic through Milwaukie. Portland wasn't even designated as a stopping point en route.

Yet the Portlanders, with what seemed incredible optimism, went on with their plans. The sawmill was finished and started turning out plank. As the worst mudholes were patched on the Canyon Road more farmers hauled wheat over the hill. The wheat piled up in the warehouses, but the Portland merchants kept buying it. How did they propose to move their wheat to the world market?

The answer came one day in the form of a beautiful ship— a steamship, *not* one of the Pacific Mail fleet—which steamed calmly up the river and tied up at the Portland dock! She was the *Golden Hunter,* the first ocean-going steamship to come this far up the Willamette. Her arrival caused a tremendous sensation along the river.

The *Golden Hunter* took on a cargo of wheat, departed— and shortly thereafter a florid-faced, cold-eyed gentleman stepped ashore on Front Street and inquired for the proprietors of the Portland townsite. He was the new manager of the Pacific Mail on the Columbia. He was soon in conference with Lownsdale and Coffin and he wasted no words.

"I'll come directly to the point, gentlemen. My company will not tolerate a competing line on the Columbia."

"Steve," Lownsdale said smilingly, "it sounds like the gentleman would like to play a little poker. Shall I oblige him?"

"Sure," Steve agreed. "The sky's the limit."

"Very well. My dear sir," Lownsdale said, "did you use the word 'tolerate'?"

"And I mean exactly that. Who owns the *Golden Hunter?*"

"We do."

"You?" Their visitor laughed unpleasantly. "You started a tannery here, I think, Lownsdale?"

"That's correct. It's an excellent and thriving tannery."

"But it doesn't qualify you to operate a steamship line, of course. And Mr. Chapman's a lawyer, I believe. As for Coffin here——"

"I build roads," Coffin said, chuckling. "Plank roads."

The steamship man was not amused. "Gentlemen, you can't fight the Pacific Mail! Come, we'll buy the *Golden Hunter*—at a reasonable price."

"Sorry," Lownsdale said. "She isn't for sale."

"Otherwise we'll cut rates to the bone! We'll drive her off the river!"

"That sounds very alarming, doesn't it, Steve?"

"It sure does. Maybe we better sell."

"Very well, sir," Lownsdale said. "We'll sell on one condition."

"*We* name the conditions. . . . But what did you have in mind?"

"That the Pacific Mail move its terminus up here to Portland."

"Oh no, that's out of the question. We're already located at St. Helens. The Tuality farmers are bringing their stuff there. The rest of it will come through Oregon City and Milwaukie. This village will never amount to anything. . . . You're not serious?"

"Certainly. We're the fastest-growing town on the river. We're at the head of deep water."

"And we've got a road planked up the canyon," Coffin put in.

"I'm not interested in your sales talk, gentlemen! Do you think we're amateurs in the shipping business? We *know* what we're doing. . . . Well? Is this your final word?"

"Can you think of anything, Steve?" Lownsdale asked.

"I sure can! Mr. Pacific Mail, I'll bet you a new silk hat——"

"Never mind," Lownsdale said. "It appears that we've already placed our bets, Steve."

The partners had invested all their cash resources in the *Golden Hunter*. It had been less than half the purchase price; the balance had been subscribed by friends along the river. It was a long chance, but for a few short weeks in the spring of '51 the future looked rosy, indeed.

The *Golden Hunter* came and went. Wagon traffic increased from the Tualatin Plains, and the settlers extended the road down into the productive heart of the valley. The town grew slowly. Farmers were spending more and more in the stores.

Then the partners learned what it meant to defy a giant like the Pacific Mail. After her fourth trip the *Golden Hunter* failed to return from San Francisco. Lownsdale hurried down to investigate—and returned completely downhearted.

"Well, Steve, they've cut our throats. The Pacific Mail's got control of the *Golden Hunter*."

Steve was incredulous. "You mean our friends sold out their stock?"

"They were offered two prices for it—and sworn to secrecy. I'm sure they didn't realize what they were doing."

"But those pirates can't take her off this run! We'll fight 'em in the courts! We'll get Chapman on it——"

"It's too late," Lownsdale said. "They've already sent her down to South America. We'll never see her again."

It was true. The *Golden Hunter* was sold down in South America at a fraction of her cost, and she never again plowed up the Columbia. The partners had lost their capital and had to sell many townsite lots to get out of debt.

Strangely, the lots continued to sell. Newcomers bought them and built on them. The demand for lumber increased, and some enthusiast started another steam sawmill. More wheat rolled in over the Canyon Road, and a surplus began to pile up. Even that didn't start a panic: two gristmills got under way, one of them the largest on the river!

One day a tall, well-dressed, courteous stranger walked into the partners' office. He introduced himself as Henry Corbett from New York. He had brought a large stock of merchandise around the Horn and was looking for a good location. He had already investigated the other leading settlements on the river. Portland was the last on the list.

Coffin began to extol Portland with his usual enthusiasm, but Corbett cut him off politely.

"Let me ask a few questions, Mr. Coffin, then I'll look the town over. What's your population?"

"Around five hundred. A lot of farmers trade here too."

"Where do farmers come from? You're in the middle of the forest."

"But the valley's just over the hill! We've got the shortest road to it! D'you know how big the valley is—how many farms?"

"Yes, I have those figures." Corbett smiled. "Every town on the river claims to be the gateway to it. . . . I think I'll look at your road, Mr. Coffin. Which direction is it?"

"South. I'll take you over there."

"No, no—I prefer to go alone, thank you. I'll see you later."

Coffin knew this was bad salesmanship. No Easterner could be expected to look over Portland's log cabins and stumps—and the rutted and patched Canyon Road—and be enthused about the city's future.

But Corbett was no ordinary Easterner. He went over the town—which was six blocks wide and four deep. He went up to the highest point in the clearing and looked out over the river. He went up to Lownsdale's tannery and over to Canyon Road and walked back into town thoughtfully.

On Front Street, bordering the river, he talked to a farmer

who was just preparing to leave town, his wagon loaded with provisions.

"I beg your pardon—I'm a stranger here," Corbett greeted him. "Could you tell me a little about the valley?"

The farmer was jovial. "The valley's a big subject, mister."

"Good land, is it?"

"*Good land?* Say, just stick your head into that gristmill and look at the wheat I fetched in today! You never saw anything like it back East! She runs better than fifty bushels to the acre down in Yamhill County."

"Yamhill? Isn't that pretty far away?"

"Shore. But I got plenty of time."

"How's this road over the hill?"

"Stranger," said the farmer, "that's the most miserable, gosh-awful road this side of Missouri! I dunno why I ever come near it!"

"Well, why *do* you? Why not take your stuff to St. Helens?"

"Too far," said the farmer with disgust. "That road's too danged steep and crooked."

"Well, why not take your wheat to Oregon City? Or Milwaukie?"

"Too much trouble. First you take it down the Tualatin River, then it's got to be hauled a piece, then loaded into a boat on the Willamette. Then it's got to be portaged past the falls. Life's too short. Why not bring it here direct?"

"In other words, it's easier to bring it here—in spite of the Canyon Road?"

"Yeah." The farmer chuckled. "As a matter of fact, that road ain't too bad since they got the worst holes planked. . . . Say, what's your line? You're no farmer."

"No, I'm a merchant. Well, thank you, sir."

"Wait a minute! You going to put in a new store? What kind of goods?"

"General merchandise—if I locate here. Crockery. Hardware. Harness."

"And dress goods?"

"Oh yes. And shoes. And sundries."

"That's the ticket!" said the farmer enthusiastically. "It's about time! I've been trying to get my woman to trade here. Where'll you be located?"

"Well"—Corbett hesitated—"I hadn't really decided——" Then he spoke strongly. "Yes, I *have* decided! I ought to be opened up in another week somewhere along Front Street. Just tell your friends to ask for Corbett's Store!"

That chance talk with an unknown farmer was the deciding point with Corbett. He leased an unfinished building at Front and Oak streets, promising to pay an unheard-of rent —$125 a month! Rival communities were staggered. Corbett was no local promoter, no townsite enthusiast. He was a shrewd merchant, and he had wagered a thirty-thousand-dollar stock of goods—the finest that had yet appeared in the Northwest—that uncouth, unpainted, stump-dotted Portland was the promising site on the river!

The most astounded of all was the manager of the Pacific Mail, when Corbett returned to St. Helens and reported his decision.

"You can't be serious, Corbett! You want your stuff unloaded at *Portland?* I thought you planned to locate where there was a future?"

"That's correct. Portland's growing fast."

"But it's just a flash in the pan! It'll collapse overnight! Why, *we* don't even stop there!"

"You will, I think, and very soon," Corbett said. "I'm no shipping expert, of course. I'm a merchant. But I've noticed that wherever there's cargo, and deep water alongside, the third thing that invariably shows up is—ships."

"But where's cargo coming from in Portland?"

"From the Willamette Valley. Somebody in Portland—I don't know who—was smart enough to improve the road over the hill. It's the shortest outlet from the valley—and it happens to strike the river at the head of deep water. That point happens to be Portland." Corbett chuckled. "I sound like a promoter myself!"

The shipping expert shrugged. "Well, you're doing the gambling. I hope your store makes out."

"I think it will. I've a feeling I ought to gross around three thousand dollars a month before long."

So Corbett moved in and set up shop, and more and more farm wagons rolled over the hill. Most important, the farm women came with the wagons. Portland was a good place to trade. You could buy anything you wanted—lumber, flour, leather goods, dress goods, hardware. In addition to Corbett's Store—which was soon grossing over three thousand dollars a month—there was C. H. Lewis's big grocery store, and others were springing up like mushrooms. It seemed there was a new store open for business each time you came to town!

All the land around the townsite was soon taken up. Even the steep slopes of Council Crest became valuable as residential property. They filled in the swamps to the north. The town was growing in all directions. Three churches went up, and a school was started.

Then came the greatest day of all: when the Pacific Mail moved its terminus up to Portland! Appropriate speeches marked that gala event. Several of the town's leading citizens, and particularly those sterling gamblers—Coffin, Lownsdale, and Henry Corbett—enjoyed a quiet chuckle as the manager of the Pacific Mail, one of the orators of the day, explained how unerringly *he* had foretold this milestone in Portland's career.

"This moment was inevitable," he told the assembled throng. "We of the Pacific Mail knew it. We knew from the beginning that Portland was the city of destiny! How did we know it?" He shrugged deprecatorily. "That happens to be our business, my friends—to sense in advance the trends of seagoing commerce! . . . The formula is simple. It has created all the world's great ports. This is it—wherever there's cargo, and deep water alongside, the third thing that invariably shows up is—ships! . . . You've supplied the cargo, gentlemen. We will furnish the ships—the modern, beautiful, ocean-going steamships of the Pacific Mail!"

1850 – Interlude

In Oregon City, in May of 1850, occurred one of the spectacular events of the crowded decade. It was the trial of the five Cayuse warriors responsible for the Whitman massacre more than two years before.

The Cayuses had learned what it meant to make war on the whites. It had been a savage lesson. They had lost many of their fighting men, had been driven from their hunting and grazing grounds, and were close to starvation; and the peace treaty required them to deliver the five warriors over to the white men.

The three-day trial began at Oregon City on May 22. Hundreds of settlers were there, many of them impatient with all this formality. These Cayuse murderers were obviously guilty; why not hang them and have done with it? Hundreds of Indians came to watch the white man's formal death ceremonies, and they, in turn, were watched narrowly by the settlers. All combined to set a grim, colorful stage.

The true drama occurred behind the scenes: the manner in which the five unrepentant Cayuses reacted to the thing which these affable, inscrutable, conquering white men called —justice.

XVIII

ONCE TO EVERY WARRIOR

THE Whitman massacre occurred on November 20, 1847. Not until the spring of 1850, at the close of the Cayuse war, were the five Indian leaders in that brutal crime brought to trial at Oregon City, seat of the Oregon territorial government.

The five prisoners were delivered to Oregon City by the military and there turned over to Joseph L. Meek, the United States marshal. Meek had a place ready for them—a small frame building on the brink of the falls, connected to the bank by a narrow causeway. Escape or rescue was next to impossible from such a spot.

Meek had waited a long time for this event. He had, in fact, dreamed about it. He was a resplendent figure in white buckskin, with his badge of office glittering on his breast and a pistol and knife at his belt. The five Cayuses were bronzed and erect. They carried themselves haughtily in the presence of their enemies, prepared to meet death as warriors should.

The most important of the five was young Tomahas, known as "The Murderer." Tomahas had personally killed Dr. Whitman with his war ax, first striking the doctor from behind, then again and again as the kindly missionary lay helpless at his feet. The four others, as minor chiefs, had directed the general slaughter that had followed.

Meek knew all five renegades, and they knew him, but no sign of recognition passed between them during the formalities of transfer, or while Meek was escorting them to

233

their quarters. The enormous crowd remained on the bank except for an alert, self-assured man named Pritchett, who followed Meek and his prisoners out on the causeway.

After the five warriors were in their cell Meek turned to look inquiringly at Pritchett. Pritchett wasn't a settler. He was secretary of the territory, a political appointee of President Polk.

"What d'ye want, Pritchett? I've got to talk to these boys—tell 'em how we do business and all that."

"Oh, you talk their language?" Pritchett spoke with a touch of condescension. "Of course! I'd forgotten your wife is a Nez Percé."

"Oh, shore. I've been to plenty of their powwows."

"Good! Then you can do some interpreting for me. You know I'm defending them at the trial."

"Yeah?" Joe eyed him sourly. "Making a little political hay, are you, Pritchett? Get the court interpreter, then. Talk to Judge Pratt."

"That won't be necessary, I'm sure. After all, I'm secretary of the territory, Meek."

"And this is Federal business, my friend! Don't throw your weight around here! Go on ashore. See Judge Pratt. Get along, now!"

Pritchett went ashore, greatly annoyed. The five prisoners hadn't understood what was said, but their black eyes glittered with amusement. They knew Joe Meek to be a happy warrior. It was now plain that he had much authority among these lesser whites.

Joe explained the procedure to them in their own tongue. They were prisoners, but they would be well fed, well cared for, until the trial. The trial, Joe explained, was a very formal and important council, held before all the people. One white man, a great orator, would describe the crimes the prisoners had committed—and another white man, also a great orator, would assert loudly and with an appearance of great earnestness that they were innocent. Then twelve white men, selected for the purpose, would weigh everything that had been said and decide whether they were guilty or innocent.

Joe spoke gravely, in the formal phrases used by the Cayuses in their council of chiefs.

"And now—is it understood? Tomahas, have you questions to ask?"

"We are greatly puzzled, Joe Meek," Tomahas replied. "We have killed your medicine man, Whitman. His blood is on our hands. Why do you give us food to eat and this good lodge in which to sleep?"

This was somewhat obscure to Joe himself, but he explained patiently: "Because you are innocent until the twelve white men say you are guilty in the great council I have spoken of."

"But *we* say we are guilty. We do not deny it. Why, then, must they hold a great council to decide it?"

Joe Meek shook his head. "You have your customs, Tomahas. We have ours. This is the white man's custom. Are there more questions?"

The five Indians whispered together in a corner. Joe Meek watched them with grim and understanding amusement. He knew the Indian viewpoint thoroughly. They had come here fortified against whatever tortures the white men might inflict upon them. Now, having been treated with kindness, they were bewildered—and completely suspicious.

Finally Tomahas spoke again.

"We will wait and see, Joe Meek. . . . Tell us this, however. Your squaw is a Nez Percé. The Nez Percés are brothers to the Cayuses. Therefore, you are our brother?"

"No. I am *blood* brother to the whites. You have killed my people."

"But you will speak truth to us always?"

"Yes, you may rely upon me. I will speak only truth."

235

Tomahas inclined his head. "Very well. We are alone among our enemies. We will rely upon you."

Their bewilderment became tinged with contempt while waiting for the trial. Their two defense attorneys—Clairborne and Pritchett—called upon them with the court interpreter, but they refused to talk unless Joe Meek stood by. They called their attorneys "big voices"—indicating their disdain—and were insulted by the suggestion that they plead not guilty.

"What do these big voices mean?" Tomahas demanded. "Are they making sport with us? Shall we say we are *not* guilty when the twelve men in the great council will know we are lying?"

"It is the white man's custom, Tomahas."

"But there will be those in the council who *saw* my war ax kill the medicine man, Whitman! . . . Very well, Joe Meek. If you say it is so, it is so."

When the trial began the primitive courtroom was crowded. It was a beautiful day—May 22, 1850—and the windows were left open for the benefit of hundreds of spectators massed outside. The five prisoners sat on a bench, facing Judge Pratt. The jury was at the judge's right, the prosecution and defense attorneys at his left. The witnesses—many of them survivors of the Whitman massacre—sat on long benches that flanked the wall.

The star witness was a sixteen-year-old girl named Catherine Segar. Catherine, or "Cathy," had been fourteen at the time of the massacre, but she had witnessed it all, and each detail was etched indelibly on her mind. She told how Tomahas had killed Dr. Whitman. She described Mrs. Whitman's death, and the manner in which her two older brothers were killed before her eyes. She described with terrible clarity how unarmed white men were shot as they ran toward shelter and wounded men were beaten with war clubs as they lay weltering in their own blood. She told of the little children, the ones with the measles, burning with fever, lying on the ground through the long night in the bitter wind, crying for water. Her baby sister had died the second day. Two other little girls—half-breeds—had died the third day from fever, thirst, and starvation.

Joe Meek translated all this, his ordinarily good-natured face twisted into bitter lines. Tomahas was more and more scornful of the white man's customs.

"Do they listen to the words of half-grown squaws?"

"*This* little squaw was there, Tomahas."

"And these twelve men—they are not warriors. I have been watching them. They looked at us fiercely only once. It was when the little squaw told about the little ones who died on the third day!"

Joe Meek nodded. "They do not like to hear that little children lay on the frozen ground in the dark night, calling for water."

"What are little girls? They will never be warriors. And one of them was a Shoshone!"

"That is correct, Tomahas," Joe Meek said. "Yes, one of them was a Shoshone."

The argument began on the second day. The prosecutor's summation was brief. He pointed out quietly that the Cayuse tribe itself had designated these five as the murderers. Witnesses had identified them—actual witnesses of the massacre. The facts spoke for themselves.

The defense had a field day. Clairborne opened with an impassioned plea on a point of law—that Oregon hadn't even been a territory at the time of the massacre. Therefore, this court had no jurisdiction. Then Pritchett took the floor. He had political ambitions, and this was the largest crowd ever assembled in the valley. He ranted and roared, striking the table with his clenched fist.

"I say to you, gentlemen, that these five defendants are guilty of no crime by any yardstick of justice! In their view the massacre was an act of war—the first blow struck in defense of their hunting grounds. We have already defeated and humbled the Cayuse tribe. Why should we take further revenge on the bodies of these unfortunate savages?"

The eyes of the five renegades glittered with amusement when this argument was explained to them. Kindness had no place in the Cayuse code. Pity was a synonym for weakness. When they had returned to their quarters that night Tomahas put his contempt into words.

"There are two kinds of white men. Some are mighty warriors. They followed us over our own trails and fought us on our own ground. When we charged they did not retreat; they killed many of us and our horses—and laughed. *Such* men we respect."

"And the others, Tomahas?" Joe prompted.

"These others are squaws. They do no fighting. They have seen no blood. They are soft. Yet *they* are the ones who make the big talk in your council!"

"Like this big voice, Pritchett? . . . Yes, I have noticed that, Tomahas. In war we fight without mercy. In the councils of peace, after the victory is won, we are always soft."

"We are warriors, Joe Meek! Let warriors judge us! We are ready to die!"

Joe Meek chuckled, though his eyes held no mirth. "Be patient, my friend. If the twelve men say you are guilty, you will die."

"At the hands of warriors?"

"Yes. A warrior will be your executioner."

The case went to the jury on the third day. In a little over an hour they returned with their verdict—guilty. . . . And still, to the annoyance of the prisoners, the big talk went on. Joe explained what it was about: the big voice, Pritchett, was asking for a *new* council. He was talking about appealing to the greatest council of all, beyond the mountains at a place called Washington.

But all these motions were overruled and the prisoners were sentenced. They were impressed by this ceremony. They stood erect, facing the judge. Joe Meek stood with them, and the room grew very quiet while the judge spoke. Nine days hence, on June 2, they would be hanged by the neck until dead.

The judge asked them if they understood the sentence. They replied through Joe Meek that they did. Did they have anything to say? With the eyes of hundreds upon them they stood haughty and silent.

But when they were safe in their cell—safe from the curious eyes of the soft ones—Tomahas turned on Joe fiercely.

"There must be no hanging, Joe Meek! Let them use knives! Let them use rifles! . . . We have relied upon you. You have given us your word!"

"When did I say you would *not* be hung, Tomahas?"

"You said a warrior would be our executioner!"

"That is correct. And he will hang you."

"But hanging is for thieves who crawl in the night! It is for cowards who cheat and lie! It is for the coyotes at heart! *We* are warriors!"

"Cowards killed Whitman when he carried no weapon," Joe said sternly. "Crawling snakes killed his squaw. Coyotes at heart let little ones die in the lonely night. calling for water."

Tomahas gestured his disgust. "That is war. Are you soft too, Joe Meek? Let us talk to our executioner. He will understand!"

"You have already talked to him. He understands—and you understand him." Joe Meek smiled a little. "*I* am the executioner, Tomahas."

The scaffold was built in the open so the public could view the spectacle. Day by day the prisoners could hear the sound of hammers and saws above the roaring of the falls. Various ladies' societies sent delegations to Joe Meek. They asked him how he could bear to take the lives of his fellow men. Wouldn't it be a load on his conscience?

Joe explained cheerfully that the jury had found the prisoners guilty, the judge had sentenced them, and it was the duty of the United States marshal to carry out the sentence. Joe Meek wasn't squeamish about doing his duty!

The night before the day of execution, as Joe stepped ashore from the causeway, Pritchett took form in the shadow. Nobody was near by, but Pritchett spoke cautiously.

"Listen, Joe. I'm acting governor of the territory now that General Lane had to leave for the south. These Indians can be useful to you and me. I think I'll grant them a stay of execution."

Joe eyed him fixedly. "Yeah?"

"Yes. That will give us time to take them back to Washington on appeal. You have some axes to grind back there, haven't you? Of course! And it'll attract the attention of the whole country. . . . Now look—I'll give you an order tomorrow. As soon as the crowd's gathered you read the order——"

"Hold on!" Joe interrupted. "The deal's off!"

"This is official, Meek! You can't disregard——"

"Listen to *me*, Pritchett. Don't you know *anything* about Indians? Let these boys get away after promising to hang them, and what happens? Inside of thirty days we're jumped by every tribe around us. They'd figure we'd *all* gone soft!"

"Nevertheless, it's your duty——"

"It's my duty to hang these varmints—and hang they shorely will! . . . Scat, now! Get away from me! Doggone, do I have to hire a rat terrier to keep you out of my way?"

The next day—and it was a beautiful summer day—the place of execution was crowded long before the appointed hour. Many blanketed Indians were there, stolid and impassive. Many settlers, equally impassive, quietly took up their positions among them. Some of these frontiersmen had fought in the Cayuse war. Some had lost brothers and sons in the campaign. Some, like Joe Meek, had helped bury the bones that prowling wolves had left among the ruins of Whitman's mission.

These were not soft men; and Joe Meek, surveying the scene with a cheerful, experienced eye, knew there would be no trouble from the Indians.

The five prisoners walked erectly into public view, their bronzed, hollow cheeks impassive. Not once during the nine days had they renewed their pleas for a more honorable death. But as they drew near the scaffold between solid walls of spectators Tomahas spoke bitterly.

"There are so *many* soft ones! Must they gather like crows to see five warriors die?"

"It will be over quickly," Joe returned. "Make your hearts strong."

"You have a knife, Joe Meek."

"No, you must hang."

"How can we face our friends in Spirit-Land with no wounds on our bodies and with the marks of a *rope* around our necks?"

In spite of his spiritual armor, Joe was a little touched. "It is only shame, Tomahas? You are not afraid?"

Tomahas gave him a glance of bleak surprise. "Who fears death?"

"Very well," Joe said. "There is no shame here. I will tell you why—after we climb up to the hanging place."

The scaffold, reared above the crowd, had a grim and awesome appearance. Rough steps led up from the rear. In front of the high platform five ropes were suspended from an overhead beam. The trap door was hinged at the back and at its front was supported by a single rope lashed to one of the upright posts. When Joe cut this rope the five would fall together.

The preliminaries at the foot of the scaffold were soon over, and Joe and his prisoners mounted to the platform.

The five took their places stoically, and Joe adjusted the ropes. They watched him, waiting. He had promised them death without shame. He came at last to Tomahas, and the young chief whispered, his lips scarcely moving:

"The knife, Joe Meek?"

"No, you must hang," Joe replied. "But listen closely. . . . If you kill your enemy's brother, or his son, or his daughter, does not your enemy say in his heart: 'I will have blood for blood?'"

The five muttered agreement. "That is true."

"Very well. When I buried the bones of the little ones who died with Whitman I said in my heart, 'I will see these warriors hung.' It was the blood oath. . . . Tell your friends *that* in Spirit-Land—and they will understand. Who can escape the blood oath?"

"But it must *be* the blood oath," Tomahas pointed out. "It must be your own flesh. Did *you* have a brother, a son, or a daughter among those who died with Whitman?"

"Yes, Tomahas. The little Shoshone who died the third night was my daughter. Her mother was my first squaw." Joe finished adjusting the noose and stepped back. "Now, is it understood? Are you ready?"

There was a pause, then Tomahas spoke for the five. "We understand. We are ready, Joe Meek."

Joe cut the rope and the five fell. The scaffold creaked. A sigh came from the assembled hundreds like a gust of wind in timber. Joe descended to the ground with a firm step and strode off through the crowd without a backward glance. His duty was done; the burying of the five bodies was a chore for lesser men.

1850 – 1852

Until 1849 the American settlers in the Oregon Country had one great objective before them. They wanted territorial status—the protection of the Federal Government, the dignity of citizenship. In their battle toward this goal they presented a united front, as they had learned to do on the overland trail.

Then, the milestone achieved, a tremendous controversy broke out in the lately peaceful valley. It was over the question: which town should be the capital of the new territory? Before it was settled some amazing and ludicrous things had happened. Actually, some enormously important issues were involved in the spectacular melee.

The colossal tempest in a teapot known as the "Capital Controversy" not only left its imprint on the political thinking of the Northwest but helped define the meaning of the word "democracy" on the national scene.

XIX

THE CAPITAL CONTROVERSY

SOON after achieving their great ambition—territorial status, in 1849—settlers in the Oregon Country made a disagreeable discovery. It was that strangers were in their midst, telling them what to do. The governor, the Supreme Court judges, and the district attorney were not local men. They were political appointees from Washington who viewed the settlers with disdain and spoke with authority.

The settlers were not immediately aware of their lost freedom. The first governor—General Joseph Lane—spoke their language. He was a quiet, kindly, neighborly man, an Indian fighter and Mexican War hero. But the general went to Congress in 1850 and was replaced by a man of entirely different character and caliber—John Pollard Gaines.

Gaines, a former Kentucky congressman and of pompous nature, was a Whig politician with definite ideas on how a primitive community like the Oregon Territory should be governed. These ideas didn't include catering either to the settlers or their rustic leaders. He believed the governing power, represented by his own somewhat fastidious person, emanated directly from Washington and was above local control.

This theory was aggravating to men who had driven oxen across the sweating plains, fought Indians, and created their own community. It was particularly annoying to two of the valley leaders, J. W. Nesmith and Asahel Bush, both forthright men. Nesmith, a burly, jovial man, had been one of the heroes of the Great Migration and a captain in the late Cayuse war. Bush was a taciturn, caustic newspaperman, intensely loyal to his friends and vindictive toward his enemies.

In November of 1850, Nesmith and Bush called on Governor Gaines at Oregon City. The pair were old cronies and had one outstanding trait in common: a sense of humor. As they approached the governor's "mansion"—a frame house adjacent to the village's main street—they were discussing the forthcoming session of the Territorial Legislature and a bill Nesmith was preparing to introduce. This bill, among other things, would move the capital of the territory from Oregon City to the larger and fast-growing city of Salem.

"I swear, I don't know what we're doing here, Bush!" Nesmith asserted. "It's our legislature, ain't it? We can introduce this bill if we've a mind to, can't we?"

"Yep," Bush said in his waspish, nasal way.

"Then why talk it over with this Gaines critter?"

"Because he sent for us."

"What of it? Have we got to come running every time he whistles from the back stoop? We can run our own business!"

"Let him find that out himself, Jim. He'll remember it longer."

"You do the talking, then," Nesmith said. "When he looks down his nose at me I feel tufts sprouting on my ears. Yeah, and thumbs on my feet. He's so doggoned smooth and superior!"

"That's just what we want. Let him feel his oats and he'll start bragging—and we'll find out what he's up to. . . . No, you lead off. I'll sit back and listen."

"I should act popeyed, eh? And a touch simple-minded?"

"That's it." Bush chuckled. "Just act natural, Jim. Sometimes you even fool me!"

The district attorney, Holbrook, was with the governor. Holbrook had a shrewd and cautious nature. He was Gaines's right-hand man, his political watchdog; and he suspected at once that these two Oregonians were not as innocent-eyed as they appeared to be. Gaines, however, saw them merely as a pair of roughly dressed, uncouth settlers.

"Well, well, Nesmith! And Mr. Asahel Bush, the distinguished editor!" Gaines's professional affability was tinged with tolerance. "I'm honored, gentlemen. What can I do for you?"

Nesmith blinked at him. "Didn't you send for us, Governor?"

"Oh yes, to be sure. What was it about, Holbrook? It's slipped my mind for the moment."

"It's that bill Nesmith's introducing next week."

"You mean my bill telling where the state buildings go?" Nesmith asked eagerly. "I figured that it's a good bill, Governor. It kind of scatters things around. Portland gets the penitentiary, Marysville gets the college, and the capitol goes to Salem. The way the boys feel——"

"That's enough, Nesmith," the governor cut in. "Never mind how the boys feel. You might as well toss that measure into the wastebasket. I'm going to oppose it."

Nesmith turned sadly to Bush. "You hear that, Bush? He's going to oppose it, he says."

"Maybe we can persuade him to see it our way, Jim."

"Impossible!" Gaines said. "You 'statesmen' down at Salem are entirely too ambitious. The capitol stays right here at Oregon City."

"You hear that, Bush? Doggone, that was such a fine bill! Mr. Gaines, can't I even introduce it?"

"Introduce anything else you like, Nesmith. This bill's illegal on the face of it. I'll point that out in my message as soon as you convene next week."

"What's illegal about it? Haven't we got the right——"

"Wait, Jim," Bush cut in gloomily. "You wouldn't argue with the governor, would you?"

Nesmith sighed. "That's right. I keep forgetting he's the

247

Moses out here in these Oregon bulrushes. . . . Let's get out of here."

Both rose to go. Bush said: "Then we can depend on a message from you, Governor?"

"If you introduce the bill—yes, without fail. Good day, gentlemen."

Gaines was much pleased with his summary handling of Nesmith and Bush. He explained to Holbrook that there was a principle at stake. These backwoods politicians might as well learn right at the beginning who held the whip hand in the territory. He'd welcome the chance to set this particular pair on their heels. The "illegality" of the bill, of course, was merely a convenient pretext.

"As a matter of fact, I hope Nesmith introduces his bill. We'll make a public show of our strength."

"Don't underestimate Nesmith," Holbrook warned.

"That yokel?"

"He has a friend in Congress. General Lane."

"General Lane has no influence in Congress!" Gaines said pityingly. "This is a Whig administration!"

"Bush never gives up. His paper gives him weight."

"You mean the *Oregon Statesman?*" Gaines laughed. "We'll set the *Oregonian* on him. A battle between these rural journalists should be amusing. . . . No, Holbrook, just leave everything to me. These primitive types are easily overawed. You know, we have a name for them down in the South. We call them 'hillbillies.' "

The legislature convened ten days later, and Nesmith immediately introduced his capital bill. The governor promptly sent over a message condemning it. Gaines also included some unasked advice as to where and how the Federal appropriation for public buildings should be spent.

The legislators viewed this message with outraged astonishment—as Nesmith and Bush had known they would. The capital question was immediately overshadowed by a more burning issue: who was this Governor John P. Gaines—this Whig, this Federalist—who dared to interfere with the legis- lative processes of the sovereign Territory of Oregon? The cry was taken up by Bush in the *Oregon Statesman*. It echoed and re-echoed through the valley.

The legislature approved Nesmith's capital bill. They did more than that: when they adjourned, they decided to recon- vene in Salem the next year.

All this was amusing to Gaines.

"Really, Holbrook, these amateur legislators have much to learn. They seem to have forgotten they have a Supreme Court. They'll find they can't legally convene in Salem."

"*If* the Supreme Court agrees with us."

"I'm sure they will. Pratt will dissent, of course, being a local man. But we'll have Justices Nelson and Strong with us. They're both good Whigs."

Oddly, Gaines had guessed right. The Supreme Court met the next spring and decided, two to one, that the statute mov- ing the capital to Salem was void. Justices Nelson and Strong, the Whig appointees, wrote lengthy opinions on the subject. Judge O. C. Pratt dissented at equal length. . . . But the majority had handed down the decision: the capital must remain at Oregon City.

Bush led a great outcry against this decision. He began a personal attack on Gaines and the majority members of the Supreme Court. The *Weekly Oregonian* in Portland, having Whig leanings, supported Gaines. In sheer ferocity and li- belous content, the resultant newspaper battle has few equals in American journalism.

The valley was split into two hostile camps, as Gaines had planned. For the first time there were two political parties in Oregon. There were the Democrats, led by the so-called "Salem gang"—of which Nesmith and Bush were the jovial ringleaders—and the Whig, or Federalist, party, led by Gaines and his supporters.

Though he had himself planned to "divide and conquer," Gaines was driven almost wild by Bush's attacks. Nevertheless, he gritted his teeth and waited for the legislature to convene. According to the Supreme Court decision, they *must* convene in Oregon City.

But one day Holbrook hurried in with astounding news.

"Listen to this, Governor. They've decided to defy the Supreme Court! They're going to meet in Salem, anyway!"

"Oh no, Holbrook. Naïve as they are, they know better than that. The session wouldn't be legal. Whatever they did would have no standing."

"There'll be legal complications," Holbrook warned. "Why not get the opinion of the United States Attorney General?"

Gaines thought a moment, then nodded. "You're right. The Attorney General will support me without question. We'll get his opinion at once. . . . We'll spike *all* their guns, Holbrook! We've got friends in the legislature. Have them convene here at Oregon City."

"But we won't have a quorum."

"It's just for the record! The Supreme Court's here. All the federal offices are here. With the legislature meeting here, this *is* the seat of government! No, they won't dare meet at Salem."

Daring men were leading the revolt, however. In the fall of '51 they did meet at Salem—all but five of the legislators. These five—four from the House and one from the Council—showed up doubtfully at Oregon City and reported to Gaines. He insisted that they convene, for the record; and a ridiculous situation ensued.

The four members of the House met solemnly each day. The lone member of the Council held equally solemn proceedings—putting motions, seconding them, voting. . . .

The hero of this singlehanded assembly was a solemn Whig councilman named Columbia Lancaster. His august deliberations convulsed the spectators.

"The Council of the Oregon Territorial Legislature will come to order," Lancaster would intone as presiding officer. "The clerk will call the roll. . . . Mr. Columbia Lancaster? . . . Here. . . . The Chair now recognizes Mr. Columbia Lancaster. . . . Mr. Chairman, I move that Mr. Columbia Lancaster be empowered and instructed to draft a memorial to the Congress of the United States on a subject of his choice. . . . Does the Chair hear a second? . . . Second. . . . It has been moved and seconded that Mr. Columbia Lancaster . . ."

This pompous nonsense went on for two weeks, while the valley howled at the spectacle. Party or no party, the settlers enjoyed a good joke. Finally, purple with chagrin, Gaines had to call a halt, record or no record.

Meanwhile, the session at Salem went blandly on. Judge Pratt moved his headquarters there. The legislators adopted a memorial to Congress condemning Gaines and Holbrook— and stating flatly that the majority of the Supreme Court had rendered an opinion based on political considerations and were therefore unfit to hold judicial positions. In strong language the memorial asked Congress to ratify the act which moved the capital to Salem.

Gaines could only wait, burning with impatience, for the opinions of his friend, the United States Attorney General. Mails were slow in those days, but finally, early in '52, the opinion arrived. It upheld Gaines. It declared Oregon City to be the lawful seat of government in the territory. All actions taken at Salem were void!

Gaines was swollen with triumph. He called in Holbrook to enjoy the fruits of victory.

"It's a long lane, Holbrook! These yokel politicians will defy *me*, will they?"

"Shall I invite them down from Salem to hear the verdict?"

"No, we'll just publish it. Let them fry in their own fat! They'll soon be here—with their hats in their hands."

But the "Salem gang," mysteriously, didn't come to Oregon City. What was even stranger, Asahel Bush had little to say in his *Oregon Statesman*. Gaines fumed and fretted. The triumph of his own party wasn't enough. He wanted his enemies—and particularly Nesmith and Bush—to confess defeat and ask forgiveness.

"You understand their mentality," he complained to Holbrook one day. "What's the meaning of this? Why haven't they come to me? Don't they understand that the opinion of the Attorney General is final?"

"Oh, they're busy men in the spring. They're probably plowing, and so forth."

"But Bush isn't a farmer. What's he up to?"

"We'll find out, I'm afraid." Holbrook chuckled. "Don't expect too much of these Indian fighters, Governor."

"They don't lose gracefully, eh?"

"Gracefully? They just don't lose!"

They came finally—Nesmith and Bush—striding up the walk together. Gaines watched them through the window, both delighted and puzzled. They didn't look worried or even embarrassed. Nesmith was as innocent-eyed as ever. Bush's truculent face was almost benevolent. . . . Strange men, these Oregonians! Didn't they even *recognize* defeat?

Holbrook let them in, his face expressionless. Knowing this pair, he was ready for anything. But Gaines couldn't keep the triumph from his voice. He had waited a long time for this moment.

"Well, well, Nesmith! And Bush, our distinguished editor! Gentlemen, I'm greatly honored."

Nesmith blinked at Bush. "Bush, he sounds just like the last time we talked to him."

"Yep," Bush said. "Howdy, Governor."

"What can I do for you two sterling citizens?"

"You tell him, Bush," Nesmith pleaded.

"No, you tell him, Jim."

"*If* you please, gentlemen—to the point!"

Nesmith shrugged. "It don't amount to much, Governor. It's about that Federal money for our public buildings. Now that Salem's the capital, we'd ought to start figuring a little. We ain't hoggish. We aim to do what's right by you boys. Let's see, now—how much money we got in the kitty?"

There was a pause, then Gaines scowled. "*Very* funny, Nesmith! You know, of course, that the capitol will *not* be built in Salem!"

Nesmith scatched his head and turned to Bush. "Bush, is he still hollering up that same creek?"

"You've forgotten something, Jim," Bush reminded.

"Doggoned if I didn't! Why, shore—he's still thinking about that Attorney General's opinion!" Nesmith produced a paper from his pocket. "Governor, here's a copy of a joint resolution the Congress of the United States just passed. They okayed our bill moving the capital to Salem. We just got it from Washington."

"Incredible, sir!"

"Here, look it over. Joe Lane introduced it for us. *There's* a lad who can see through a split-rail fence! He knows how we like to run our own business out here, without help from these foreign experts, and doggoned if he didn't get Congress to agree with him! Yes sir, old Joe's all right. . . . Well, Governor, like I was saying——"

"One moment, Nesmith." Gaines was completely staggered. "Holbrook, it—it's true! Look—and President Fillmore *signed* it!"

"Hm-m." Holbrook read the joint resolution swiftly. "My word, Governor! This not only overrides the Attorney General—it legalizes everything they did at Salem!"

"Oh, shore!" Nesmith said. "Old Joe Lane was on the job. There's a lad . . . What's wrong, Governor?"

"Gentlemen—if you'll excuse me." Gaines rose with an effort. "I'm not feeling too well. I think I'll—retire. . . ."

There was a momentary silence after he was gone. Then Nesmith spoke with an appearance of deep concern. "Now then, Holbrook, what ails the governor? Shorely to goodness he hasn't been upset over this picayune row about the capital?"

"Perhaps," Holbrook admitted. "It may have been a contributing factor."

"Sho! After he's been in Oregon a while longer and gets to know the folks out here——"

Bush chuckled dryly. "Jim! Get down to business."

Nesmith nodded. "Holbrook's the man to talk to anyway. Now then, Holbrook, about that building fund. We got to start figuring . . ."

Yes, it was a very rough experience for John Pollard Gaines. It was a bitter pill for the Whigs to swallow. But far more important than the triumph of the Democrats and the damage to Gaines's pride was that Congress had again subscribed to the principle of local self-government. The nation was less than eighty years old in '52. Democracy itself was still on trial. Congressional action on the Oregon "Capital Controversy" was a long step forward along the as yet vaguely defined trail of states' rights.

The presidential election of '52 brought another humiliation to John P. Gaines. The Whig candidate, Winfield Scott, was badly defeated by the Democrat, Franklin Pierce. One of Pierce's first actions in '53 was to appoint a new governor for the Oregon Territory.

It was Holbrook's painful duty to break the news to Gaines.

"I've just received an official notice from Washington, Governor. It's the appointment of your successor."

"To the victor belongs the spoils, Holbrook," Gaines said grimly. "Who's the new man?" The hue of his florid face deepened. "Anybody but General Lane! That would be too much."

"I'm sorry, Mr. Gaines. Yes, it's General Lane."

Gaines fought on to the end. He retired to the valley and himself ran as delegate to Congress. He was badly defeated. The Whig party was finished nationally. It was tottering in Oregon, and a party called "Republican" was emerging from the political mists.

Gaines died three years later in Marion County. After the funeral Nesmith paid him a tribute typical of a region whose ways the late governor had never fully understood.

"You know, Bush, ornery as he was, that Gaines had his points."

"I'm trying to think of them," said the unforgiving Bush. "Name them and I'll put them in the paper."

"He never backed down. He never quit. If he'd just come out here before high society plumb ruined him, what an Indian fighter he'd have made!"

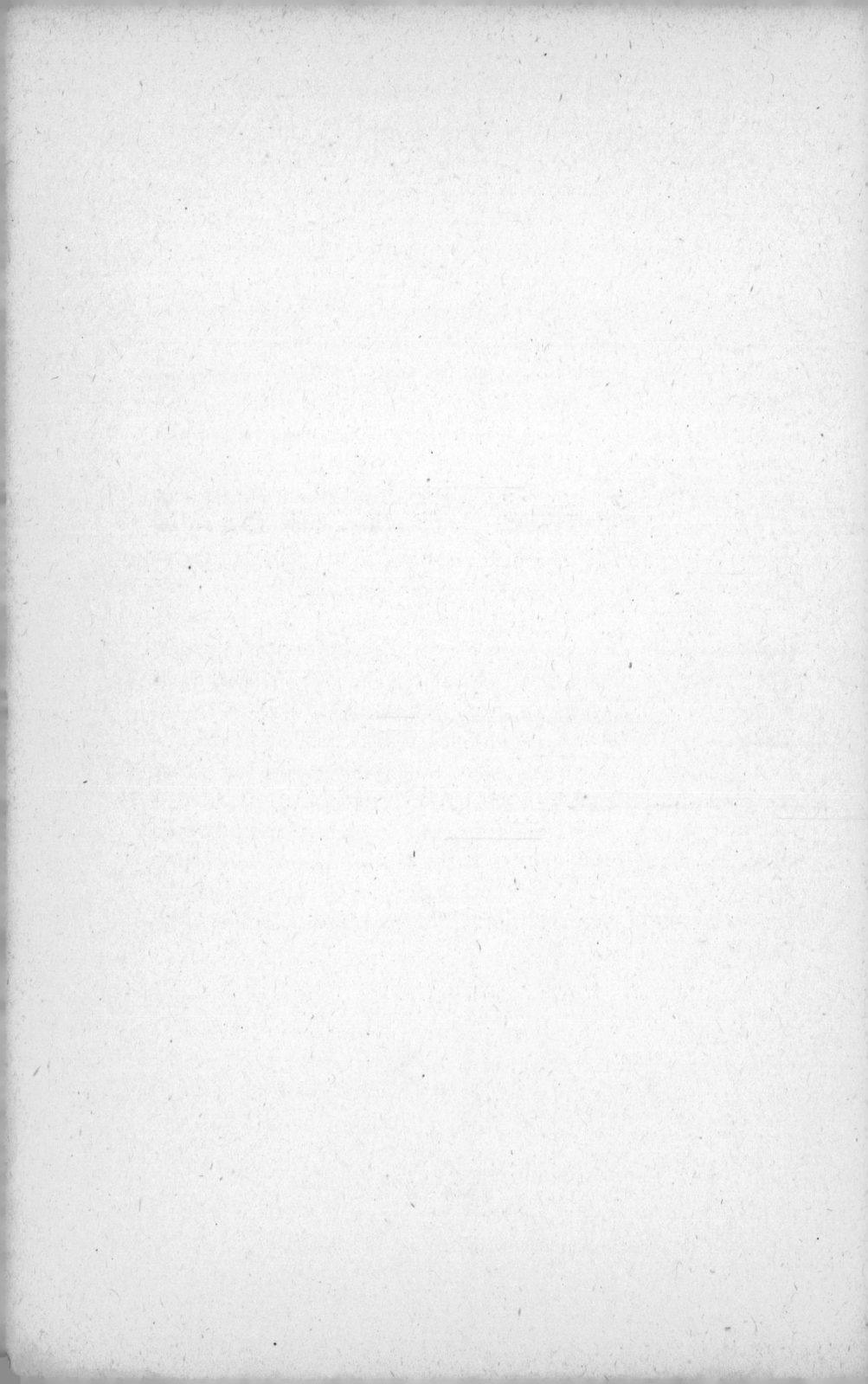

1852

In the Willamette Valley in 1852, the social center in each remote district was the community church. Such gatherings were essential on the frontier scene, apart from their spiritual value. They provided a meeting place where men discussed crops, politics, and Indian trouble, and the women paraded their best bonnets and exchanged gossip. Most delightful of all was the revival meeting. Families came miles to such an event, bringing their blankets and food with them. It was an emotional release from the workaday world.

The itinerant preachers, or "circuit riders," who made these meetings possible were as hardy as the settlers themselves. They had to be. They traveled on horseback into the farthest corners of the wilderness, facing dust and storm en route. They stopped wherever night overtook them. They held services in homes, in barns, under the spreading trees. They were empire builders in the highest sense.

One of them, Joab Powell, became known in every corner of the valley. His influence is still felt today, almost a century later. Few among his contemporaries more fully measured up to the simple but conclusive pioneer tribute: "There were men in those days."

XX

THE CIRCUIT RIDER

THEY still tell a hundred stories about Joab Powell down in the valley. Physically he was a big man even for the frontier. Though less than six feet in height, he weighed three hundred pounds—and it wasn't fat that bulged his shoulders and gave him arms thicker than the thighs of an average man. He had the strength and stamina of a grizzly, an enormous appetite, and a voice of incredible volume.

Though he could neither read nor write, Joab knew most of the Bible by heart; and when he began to "exhort" and put his force into it, sinners cringed and the very walls shook. Few men could oppose him in debate. Where is there room for abstract argument when a lion roars?

When Joab sang his voice drowned out all other near-by sounds. They said you could easily hear him two miles away in the cool of a summer evening. Throughout the Oregon Territory, in the '50s, his voice was known as "the harp with a thousand strings."

Joab was fifty-two years old when he came to Oregon by ox team with his wife and twelve children. Inquiring here and there, he decided on the Santiam section and brought his wagons to halt beside a beautiful meadow. Leaving the older boys in charge of making camp, Joab and his wife climbed to the top of a low hill to survey their free land.

Joab's wife was a small, quiet women of German ancestry. Her face was gentle and kindly. As they stood side by side looking south in the hush of sundown, some of the color harmonies in the western sky were reflected in their shining eyes.

"Well, Annie, ain't that a sight?" Even Joab's great voice was hushed. "Look at that creek shining in the meadow! Look at that timber over yonder!"

"It is very pretty, Joab. How much of it is ours?"

"Two square miles! The two big boys get half a section each. So our south line's clean over to that ridge!"

"So far as that?"

"Yep. And two miles up and down the creek—clean down to the Santiam. . . . See those groves of trees here on the left?" Joab's chuckle rumbled in his chest. "*What* d'ye reckon we'll build there, Annie?"

"I know. You will build a church."

"Yep. The grove's a natural campground. We'll baptize sinners down there in the creek. . . . The creek hasn't got a name yet, Annie. So *I'm* naming it now. It's the Jordan!"

"It is a good name."

"There ain't any better!" Joab glanced about him and lowered his voice. "Annie . . ."

"Yes, Joab?"

"This is new country. I'm starting fresh here. I *can* make a go of it—can't I?"

"Of course, dear." She spoke with complete confidence. "Nothing can stop you. You are not afraid—and you are strong."

"Why, shore!" Joab's voice rose up full and strong. "You better look for a hole to crawl into, Satan! Joab Powell's come to Oregon—and there ain't room for both of us! Give me strength, O Lord, to carry the bread of life to these starving sinners! Amen!"

"Amen," his wife echoed softly.

"Say, when did we eat last?" Joab demanded. "Hadn't we better get back to camp and get some victuals cooking?"

"You are hungry again already?"

"A man can't serve the Lord on an empty stomach, can he? Come on, honey! It seems like I haven't et for a week."

They named it the Jordan, and Jordan Creek it remained. Joab got his farm under way the next spring, and that fall he and his neighbors built a log church in the grove. They named it Providence Baptist Church—and on that site a larger Providence Church still stands today, overlooking the Jordan.

Joab's fame soon spread far and wide. People came for miles to hear him preach and sing. The "mourners' bench" was always crowded. Converts were baptized by immersion in the chill waters of the creek. Joab seemed immune to the cold—or any other hardship, for that matter. He could baptize by the hour, winter or summer, hip-deep in water that might have chilled a polar bear.

He soon got restless. It wasn't enough that sinners should come to him; he must go out in forest and field and track them down. In far corners of the valley Satan was walking the highways and byways, unaware that Joab Powell had come to Oregon.

Late in the second spring, after the wheat was in and the garden truck was all planted, Joab and his wife were sitting on the porch one evening. Joab spoke suddenly.

"Well, Annie—d'ye know what I'm going to do tomorrow?"

"Yes," she said. "I have your saddlebags packed. Your blankets are all ready to roll up."

"What? You knew I was ready to start out on the glory trail? I never said a word about it!"

"It is not necessary, my dear." She smiled a little. "Have I lived with you this long for nothing?"

"Bless your heart! . . . It's all right, is it? You can get along here with the boys?"

"Do not worry about us. Just so you're back to help with the harvest."

"I'll be back! And what a harvest the Lord will have this

261

summer! Nothing can stop me! I'll prevail against Satan wherever I go!" Then he added in a low voice: "Won't I, Annie?"

"Of *course*, Joab."

So Joab Powell started out the next day on his big roan horse. It had to be big, to carry his massive body, his saddle-bags and bedding. He took food enough for one day and one pound of chewing tobacco—enough for four days. After that the Lord would provide.

He blazed a trail wherever he went. Once seen, Joab Powell was never forgotten. Once a community heard him "exhort" and listened to him sing, he was sure of an audience as long as he wanted to stay, or as often as he chose to return.

The manner in which he gained an audience in a new community had a circus flavor, yet these were the days when there were no traveling carnivals, few amusements, few social events to enliven the drab monotony. More than one remote community in the valley—isolated from the world and hungry for diversion in a sense unknown today—was astonished and delighted at the appearance of an enormous and jovial stranger mounted on a huge roan horse, bellowing down the village street or along the rural roads:

"There'll be sarvices at Tethrow's new barn tomorrow noon! Joab Powell will praise the Lord and wrassle with the devil! Bring victuals with you! Come one, come all! . . . Sarvices at Tethrow's barn!"

Some came out of sheer curiosity. Some came to jeer—and remained to pray. They all brought food. The noon service would be the curtain raiser, the warm-up, the challenge preceding the real battle. The general get-together would follow: the eating and neighboring. By that time Joab would no longer be a stranger. Everyone would have confidence in him; and the afternoon service, when Joab really unloosed his native force, his sincerity and colossal voice would be a roaring triumph for the Lord

How could this shaggy, tobacco-chewing giant of a man cast such a spell over his listeners? It was partly because of his confident bulk. He was like a grizzly, serene in his strength, a rock planted solidly in a puny current. None of his listeners ever knew the source of his supreme self-confidence. It was the faith of a frail, indomitable little woman back there on Santiam, the one who knew no doubt, to whom he could turn for sanctuary when all else failed. *Of course, my dear, nothing can stop you. You are not afraid—and you are strong. . . .*

That confidence made his colossal voice "a harp with a thousand strings." It could plead. It could be gentle. It could thunder in wrath. And his very simplicity, his illiteracy made him easy to understand. He was talking to simple, illiterate men—and he talked their language.

He was a farmer himself and a good one. He knew all about crops and barn raisings. He knew how to repair a wagon wheel and build a hog-tight fence. He understood cattle and horses. Once, in the wilds of western Lane County, he came upon a settler standing despondently beside the road. His wagon was hub-deep in mud. One of his horses was mired down.

Joab Powell reined up and looked the situation over.

"What's wrong with your horse, brother?"

"He's plumb give out," said the settler gloomily. "I might as well shoot him and leave him lay."

"What? A sound young critter like that? Oh no! He's just discouraged. We'll soon have him out of there!"

"Stranger," said the settler, "I don't know who you are— but you just don't know horses. When they give up, they're done for. The angel Gabriel couldn't get this critter to stir an inch."

"The angel Gabriel wouldn't try to help him unless he helped himself," Joab said sternly. "He's like a man neck-deep in sin. All you can do is whisper in his ear. The rest is up to him!"

"You sound like a preacher," said the settler with disgust.

"I *am* a preacher. My name's Joab Powell. . . . Now you watch that horse help himself. Just take your bucket and dip up some water and put it in his ear."

"In his *ear*? What good'll that do?"

"Have faith, brother," Joab counseled. "Go ahead! But stand in the clear. There's going to be plenty of mud flying."

The unbelieving settler filled the bucket and poured a small trickle in the horse's ear; and that astounded animal—discouraged a moment before, seemingly beyond the will to struggle—rose up from the mud like a wounded cougar. It leaped to firm ground and danced there, snorting and tossing its head.

The settler was more astonished than the horse.

"What ailed him? I swear, I never seen a horse come alive that fast before!"

"It's simple," Joab explained. "There's only once in his life that a horse gets water in his ear—when he's about to drown. He figured he was about to drown, and right away he forgot all about how he'd done give up."

"Well, sir, there's a trick *I* won't forget! Reverend, you just wait and come along home with me, and tomorrow we'll have the neighbors in and hold services. If you know your hell-fire like you know your horses, we'll shore have a time of it!"

Yes, Joab Powell knew the ways of the frontier. He was at home with rough, simple men. He had an enormous appetite, and the settlers loved to see him eat. He liked boiled cabbage, and as the years went by folks along the circuit always had boiled cabbage waiting for him—huge steaming platters of it. They said he ate it like a good horse eats hay. Joab said it gave him strength to battle for the Lord.

He never made a show of his strength, but when the Lord gave him a chore to do he didn't side-step it. Up near Champoeg a giant blacksmith named Harper announced publicly that Joab Powell had better stay away from *this* section of the valley; it was "unhealthy for big-mouthed preachers." In due time this word reached Joab Powell—and shortly thereafter a vast commotion broke out in the little settlement.

"Fight! *Fight!* . . . There's a fight at Harper's blacksmith shop! Harper's tangling with a fat man that just rode into town! . . . Fight!"

And what a fight! The whole village gathered to see it. The stranger's coat and hat were hanging on a limb. His horse stood near by. . . . And the stranger wasn't a fat man, after all.

His shirt was torn off, and you never saw a bigger chest or more bulging muscles. He was shorter than the blacksmith, but when they came together and grappled it was the blacksmith's huge body that went sailing through the air. And when they charged like bulls the stranger was built closer to the ground, and he mowed the blacksmith down.

Finally they were rolling in the dust, and the stranger's arms closed on the blacksmith's body like a bear trap; and that was all there was to it. Harper—the unbeatable, the roaring and invincible bully—was yelling "uncle."

"That's—enough, Powell!" he gasped. "I'm licked! I'm licked, I tell you! Leggo!"

The stranger let go and got up, breathing heavily. "Well, let me give you a hand up, brother," he said. He helped the blacksmith up and supported him. "There! . . . Brother Harper—you're all right! You're the toughest critter I ever got holt of. Let me shake your hand."

"Put 'er there, Parson! . . . And listen, you folks! This here's Joab Powell, the best all-round preacher that ever lit in these parts. He's going to hold services here tomorrow—and all you miserable sinners be on hand. I'll be here! . . . How's that, Parson?"

"Praise the Lord!"

265

Moreover, he was a *gentle* man. He knew the tragedy and heartache of the frontier. He knew sorrow and death. Two of his own children had died in Missouri, and when Joab spoke at a funeral you knew, somehow, that this wasn't just another preacher doing a preacher's job. He *understood*—and had a way of making things sound like they weren't just words re-echoing in an empty room.

There was that time he preached over the Tuttle boy's grave, away back in the hills, in Scoggin's Valley. Joab had ridden sixty miles to be there. It was the one time, above all, when they needed a preacher. Besides, Joab knew the boy.

His name was Sandy; and Joab, standing by the grave, told the neighbors what a good boy Sandy had been. A *dependable* boy. When they sent him out after the cows he always found them and brought them home. When they set him to hoeing corn he hoed his row right through to the finish. He'd always kept the wood box full of kindling.

"And I ain't going to tell his folks that they mustn't grieve for Sandy. I *know* better. But I can comfort them, friends. Listen. . . . D'ye think for a minute they weren't watching for him over yonder, day before yesterday, when Sandy took out alone acrost the Jordan? Can't you just see the Lord standing there on the bank, smiling?" His enormous voice boomed: "Why, shore! . . . And you can hear the Lord telling Saint Peter, 'Never mind, now—*I* know this little pilgrim. This here's *Sandy!* . . . Now you set right up by this big window, Sandy, so you can look down there at Scoggin's Valley. So you'll be the first to see your folks coming acrost the creek—and you can get right out there on the bank and yell, "Hi, Maw! Hi there, Paw! . . . I beat you home—a little ways!"' That's it, folks. Sure Sandy's gone —but not far, and not for long. It's just acrost the creek. He just beat you home—a little ways. . . ."

In twenty years Joab baptized three thousand converts—

a greater number than that of any other evangelist of record in the valley before or since. His biggest day was when he baptized two hundred. The water was cold, and he immersed them one by one in lots of fifty—thawing out between times by a roaring fire.

He would return each fall to the Santiam, ragged and dispirited. His home was a well of strength. Each night by the fireside, throughout the winter, his wife would read a chapter of the Bible to him. Joab would listen and later repeat it word for word. Each day, quietly, she would refer with pride to his summer's achievements. Slowly his confidence and courage would build up; and in the spring, like a bear emerging from hibernation, he would go roaring forth to fresh conquests.

Each fall there were fewer of his children at the homestead. In the later years there was only his wife; and in the last year Joab knew, as soon as he saw her, that she would never live to another harvest. He knew, too, that as soon as she was gone he would never ride the circuit again.

She died in early spring. In her last moments, at her request, he sang for her. Her final words, as always, were designed to give *him* strength.

"Look out the window, Joab. Is the creek shining in the sunlight?"

"Yes, honey."

"That is the Jordan—remember? And you remember what you said at the Tuttle boy's grave? It isn't far to the other bank."

"But I'm a miserable sinner, Annie! Can I make it alone acrost the creek?"

"Nothing can stop you," she whispered. "You have fought the good fight. You will be strong and unafraid at the last— as always. . . . Say it quickly, Joab, won't you?"

"Why, shore!" Then Joab whispered: "But will you be watching for me, Annie? As close to the bank as you can get?"

"Of *course*, my dear."

So she died as she had lived—gently—and Joab Powell never rode the circuit again. In the late fall, seven months after his wife was gone, his eldest son found him on the cabin floor, his head pillowed on his arm, looking out across the meadow.

But his eyes were closing. His only struggle, at the last, was of the spirit.

"I done those things I hadn't ought to have done. And I left undone . . ." Suddenly he cried out in terror: "Lend a hand here, Lord! I'm a-sinking fast! . . . *Annie!* Why, you're right, Annie—it ain't so deep! It ain't far! . . . Give me a hand up, honey." His voice came with gathering strength. "I knew I'd make it! . . . Why, *shore!*"

1853

During the early 1850s the Oregon Territory was constantly embroiled in Indian trouble. No pitched battles were fought in the Willamette Valley itself, but warlike tribes east of the Cascades had banded together to make a last stand against the encroaching whites. In the Rogue River Valley to the south an equally fierce tribe was on the warpath. There were many campaigns and bloody encounters before peace came.

In the Rogue River campaign in 1853 occurred one of the spectacular incidents of the troubled period. It was the signing of the Treaty of Table Rock. The caliber of the settlers can find no better illustration than the story of that famous council—when eleven white men walked unarmed into a camp of seven hundred treacherous Rogue River warriors, into what appeared to be certain death, and lived to tell the tale.

XXI

THE TREATY OF TABLE ROCK

THE puzzling nature of the white men was never fully understood by the fierce and crafty Rogues. White chiefs put their trust in treaties and promises when arrows and knives were much more effective! So the Rogues signed a peace treaty in 1852—and almost immediately renewed the slaughter and looting of white settlers. In the spring of 1853 the settlers sent out another call for help. This time the whites came grimly, and in force.

A company of regulars came over from Port Orford. General Joseph Lane came down from the Umpqua with a company of fifty men. J. W. Nesmith quickly organized seventy-five volunteers in the Willamette Valley, and another company of regulars started south from Fort Vancouver. With the Vancouver men came Joel Palmer, Superintendent of Indian Affairs, and Samuel Culver, Indian Agent.

General Lane was first on the ground and met the Rogues in a minor but successful battle on Evans Creek. Then Captain Nesmith rode in with his volunteers—and was greatly annoyed to learn that General Lane had already agreed to hold a peace council with the Rogues in their stronghold at Table Rock, a great promontory which overlooked the Rogue River Valley from the east.

Nesmith, a big, jovial pioneer, believed that the only good Indians were dead Indians. Lane was small, quiet of manner, but with inflexible courage and resolution. He had been slightly wounded in the arm at the Evans Creek battle.

Their difference in rank meant nothing to Nesmith. He stated his opinion bluntly.

"You mean to say, General, that you're parleying with these varmints *again?* After they tore up the treaty you made with them last year?"

"*This* treaty has teeth in it, Captain. We'll put them on a reservation. And they'll stay there."

"But they ain't licked yet!" Nesmith protested. "Until they are—and so badly that they *stay* licked—all this talk's a waste of time. How many of the varmints are up there at Table Rock?"

"Seven hundred fighting men, I should say. It includes some Klamaths and Shastas."

"Seven hundred?" Nesmith echoed. "And you figure to parley with them and *tell* them what you've got to do? It won't work, General. You may know those Indians down Mexico way, but these Rogues will laugh at us. They figure they've got us outnumbered three to one. And they have!"

"True, but we're better armed. They know we're determined."

"Not yet they don't! . . . No, General, the thing to do is wait till the howitzer gets here, then blast 'em off that rock. Then make good Indians out of three fourths of what's left. After that, parley with 'em!"

Lane smiled. "You're too bloodthirsty, Captain. We can't slaughter these savages unnecessarily. I'm sure they'll agree to settle quietly on a reservation."

"*Before* they're licked? I'll have to see that."

"You will," the general promised. "I'm counting on you to be there, Captain."

Captain Smith rode in presently with his mounted dragoons from Port Orford. Captain Kautz appeared with his Vancouver company, dragging a twelve-pound howitzer. All encamped on the meadow below Table Rock.

The Indian stronghold seemed impregnable. It was above

a rocky slope, at the base of the perpendicular cliffs that comprised the face of Table Rock. All that night the two hundred and fifty white men could see the Rogue campfires at the base of the cliff, and seven hundred painted warriors doing their war dances by the leaping flames.

On the morning of September 10, 1853—a beautiful day—General Lane called his leaders together. In addition to his officers they included the two Indian agents, Palmer and Culver. Calmly, in his quiet way, the general outlined his orders of the day.

"Gentlemen, I've agreed with the head man of the Rogues, Chief Joe, that I'll meet him up yonder, accompanied by ten of my chiefs. We'll go up there unarmed. If we reach no agreement, they guarantee us safe conduct back here to camp. . . . Captain Nesmith, it appears that you're struggling with some unpleasant thought?"

"I sure am! We can't go up there unarmed. I *know* these Rogues! Their guarantee isn't worth a continental. They've never let a white man escape, once they got their clutches on 'em!"

"Oh, we'll leave our forces deployed here in the meadow, ready for action. The howitzer will be in position. Captain Smith's dragoons will be in company front, ready to charge."

Nesmith grinned mirthlessly. "You mean *after* our scalps are fluttering from those lodge poles up yonder?"

"Oh no. I'm sure they'll respect the terms of the armistice. For the eleven of us to go up there unarmed will impress them with our self-confidence. . . . Now, gentlemen, these are the ten who will accompany me. Mr. Palmer, and Mr. Culver, representing the government. Captains Smith and Kautz, representing the Regular Army. Captain Nesmith, representing the volunteers, who will act as our interpreter——"

"Wait a second, General," Nesmith cut in. "Just cross off the name of Captain Nesmith. He ain't a-going."

General Lane stiffened a little. "We appreciate your sense of humor, Captain—but *not* at this particular moment."

"I ain't joking, General. I'll fight these varmints morning, noon, or night. I'll do anything a good soldier's expected to do. Nothing in those specifications includes laying my rifle down and walking unarmed into that nest of snakes. That ain't fighting Indians—it's committing suicide!"

"Very well," the general said. "If the prospect's too alarming for you, Captain, we'll find another interpreter. . . .To continue, gentlemen. Lieutenants Metcalf and Mason——"

"Hold on, General!" Nesmith said angrily. "You figure I'm *scairt* to go along?"

"What impression did you wish to convey?"

"Doggone it, it's a question of judgment!"

"The question of judgment's *my* responsibility, Captain."

"All right, all right!" Nesmith threw up his hands. "I might as well be slaughtered with the rest of you! I've always wondered what it felt like to get scalped!"

"Very well. . . . Lieutenants Metcalf, Mason, and Tierney . . ."

So Captain Nesmith, certain in his heart that he would never again see his beloved Polk County, rode with the others, unarmed, across the flat. They left their horses at the foot of the slope and scrambled up through the boulders toward the Indian fort. Below them, Smith's dragoons drew up in a long line—a beautiful and impressive array, but too far away to be of help in any sudden emergency.

From above, the seven hundred Rogue warriors looked down upon them with fierce delight. To the rank and file of the painted renegades, who had been taught from childhood that cunning was a virtue second only to bravery, this was crafty old Chief Joe's greatest coup. These eleven white chiefs *were* unarmed! Without their leaders, the puny army of whites below could easily be overwhelmed and blotted out.

274

Chief Joe and one of his subchiefs, Mox-Mox, stood near the rocky barrier. Mox-Mox was an interpreter and the chief's right-hand man. He spoke exultantly to the inscrutable old warrior in the language of the Rogues.

"This is good, Chief Joe. We will make big talk—and *then* we will cut their throats?"

"No, Mox-Mox. I have a bigger plan. We will make many promises. We will sign another treaty. Then we will let them go."

Mox-Mox was incredulous. "When the rabbit is in the trap does the hunter let it go? Tell me this big plan so I will not speak with foolish tongue."

"This is the plan," the old chief said. "Our friends, the Klamaths and the Shastas, have sent warriors here to observe the white man. When they see that the white man will not fight but again puts his trust in promises and treaties, they will know that I speak the truth, and the white men *are* soft and foolish. Then the Shastas and Klamaths will join us in their full strength—and the *next* time we will kill all white men in the valley and all that are sent against us!"

"It is good!" Mox-Mox agreed. "But our warriors are ready for the kill. Will they understand the plan?"

"We will explain it as the big talk goes on. Fortunately these white chiefs do not understand our tongue. Even this smiling chief, Nesmith, can only speak Chinook, the language of the traders. . . . There, they are close now, Mox-Mox. Remember, we are Rogues!" The chief's eyes glittered with grim amusement. "Which means, in the white men's tongue, that we are truthful men."

The eleven white men scaled the barrier, and the armed and painted warriors closed about them, forming a compact circle. Two logs were in the center, and the principals sat down ceremoniously, Chief Joe and his right-hand men on one side and General Lane and his officers facing them.

The scouts from the Klamath and Shasta tribes stood in

the front rank, studying these incredible white men. Upon what strange medicine did they rely to come so trustingly, without weapons, into the full war strength of the Rogues?

The long parley began. The business of interpreting went slowly, since the trade jargon, Chinook, was the only common language. When General Lane spoke Nesmith translated into Chinook and Mox-Mox translated from Chinook to Rogue. When Chief Joe spoke the process was reversed. Thus each side could talk freely among themselves in their own tongue.

Yet there was danger in this. While Mox-Mox was translating the general's opening question—as to why the Rogues had broken the previous treaty—Nesmith spoke warningly:

"Remember, boys, these varmints can't understand the King's English, but they can sure read faces. They're watching us like hawks every minute. So don't weaken, whatever happens."

Chief Joe asserted gravely, through Mox-Mox, that the settlers, not the Rogues, had broken the peace treaty. The settlers had killed Rogues; therefore, the Rogues had killed settlers.

General Lane replied that white men must never be killed under any circumstances. The white man's law must prevail. It applied both to whites and Indians. Chief Joe retorted that the Rogues needed no law other than their own. This country belonged to the Rogues, not the white man.

Nesmith pointed out that this was a dangerous trend.

"The longer we argue, General, the more they're certain we're squaws. They know they broke the treaty. They know *we* know it. If we're going to get tough with them we'd better do it now."

"We shall, Captain," Lane said quietly. "The treaty's next."

As the general had said, this new treaty had teeth in it. Nesmith explained to Mox-Mox that since the Rogues had failed to live up to their previous treaty the tribe must now be put on a reservation. He explained what a reservation was—a part of the valley set aside for the exclusive use of the tribe, leaving the rest of the land to the whites. The Rogues would be paid for giving up their lands. From that money would be deducted all property damage the Rogues had inflicted on the white settlers.

From the Rogue viewpoint, this proposal verged on sheer impertinence. It invited them to give up their ancient hunting grounds without a struggle. It came from a soft and inferior enemy whose chiefs were already in their hands! A murmur of astonishment and anger came from the intent warriors as Mox-Mox translated. What foolish talk was this?

Wily old Chief Joe saw an opportunity to impress the Shastas and Klamaths. He said sternly to Mox-Mox:

"You are sure you have clearly understood what the white chief said?"

"Yes, and I have reported it correctly."

"Good." Chief Joe fixed his eyes sternly upon the visiting scouts. "Now our friends from the mountains can see what is in the white man's heart! First he comes among us, speaking gently, and builds his home upon our ground. Next he tells us we must obey *his* laws. Now he tells us: 'We will put a fence around you, like horses. You must stay within the fence. The rest of the ground is ours.'"

"You are right, Chief Joe," Mox-Mox whispered. "Let us forget the big plan. Let us kill these white chiefs now!"

"No," Chief Joe returned. "The big plan is best. When we are ready there will be but one battle." He raised his voice. "Listen to my words, warriors! We will accept their money. We will pretend to live in the pasture, like horses— and we will trade this money for more of the white man's rifles. Then, with our friends from the mountains, we will break out in our full strength and kill every white man in the valley!"

There was an angry uproar. The eleven white men couldn't understand the debate that followed, but a blind man could have sensed the trend of it. Chief Joe was counseling prudence—delay—but his warriors, fiercely eager for a showdown, were working themselves into a frenzy.

Nesmith spoke jovially. "It looks like they don't like it, General. If they say no—what's our next move?"

"If they insist on war, we'll have to oblige them."

"But *our* scalps will be their first order of business. . . . Oh, oh—what's this?"

A diversion came, unexpected and dangerous. An Indian runner broke into the circle, staggering with weariness. He glared fiercely at the whites, shouted his news to Chief Joe, and fell exhausted to the ground.

"Find out what's wrong, Nesmith."

"I'll go over beside Mox-Mox and Chief Joe," Nesmith said in a low voice. "Sit tight, everybody."

So Nesmith crossed the narrow circle and seated himself on the log beside Chief Joe. The Rogue warriors were crowding in, their bows and rifles aimed. The slightest gesture of fear would have been fatal. Nesmith looked at the nearest arrows smilingly, an eyebrow raised, while he whispered to Mox-Mox. The other white men stood fast. General Lane remained seated on the log, his kindly face as serene as ever.

Nesmith raised his hand for silence and spoke coolly across the circle to General Lane.

"The settlers have killed another Rogue—a sneak thief called Jim Taylor. A Captain Owens was in command. It seems they caught this Rogue varmint red-handed, tied him to a tree, and shot him plumb full of holes. You know this Captain Owens, General?"

"Yes, and I shall certainly reprimand him! I told him there must be no bloodshed until this parley was over!"

"*We'll* be so full of arrows we'll look like pincushions in about ten seconds," Nesmith said. "Scatter around a little, men, so they can't shoot us without slaughtering each other. . . . General, you'd better start making a speech!"

Nesmith remained seated on the log beside Chief Joe, certain that death was only seconds away. But he was a brave man and he was determined to run his jovial bluff to the end. There were other brave men in the circle. His companions spread apart, their backs almost touching the trembling points of drawn arrows, and stood arms folded, facing General Lane.

The general rose from the log and stood erect, his wounded arm hanging at his side. He began to speak—with decision, with utmost coolness.

"Nesmith, tell Chief Joe that Owens did wrong when he killed Jim Taylor. Tell him I will find Owens and punish him for it—and we will pay for Jim Taylor in shirts and blankets, according to the Rogue law. . . . Tell him we came here unarmed, in good faith, and that I do not believe the Rogues are cowards. Tell him they can murder us easily —but *if* they do, every Rogue warrior will be hunted from the face of the earth! Tell him that is a promise, Nesmith— —and remind him that I have never yet lied to the Rogues!"

Nesmith translated this as directed. He did it dramatically, placing his hand inside his buckskin shirt in a rhetorical gesture, leaning past Chief Joe to speak to Mox-Mox. He also added a few whispered words of his own.

For a moment Chief Joe sat motionless, looking hard at Nesmith—and Nesmith stared back, his eyes no longer jovial. Then, with a slight shrug, Chief Joe motioned to his warriors, palm outward, that there must be no killing.

The Rogue warriors were astonished and outraged, but they stood fast while the chief addressed them sternly in their own tongue:

"The white chief has promised to pay for the death of Jim Taylor. He has never lied to us. The honor of the tribe is satisfied." Then he went on with studied contempt: "Now

279

we will make soft talk about this new treaty—and our friends, the Shastas and Klamaths, will see how eager these white men are to avoid war with the mighty Rogues!"

His fierce warriors stood motionless, then discipline prevailed and the arrows lowered slowly. The parley went on and lasted for hours. In the end Chief Joe agreed to retire to the reservation and remain peaceable there. The tribe was to receive forty thousand dollars in merchandise over a period of years. On their part, the Rogues ceded twenty-five hundred square miles of the valley to the whites forever.

Chief Joe and his subchiefs gravely made their marks on the treaty. When the eleven left the barrier and started down the slope Nesmith couldn't believe the Rogues would actually let them get away. He expected a sudden yell of derision from the stronghold and arrows and bullets in their backs.

None came, and when they reached the safety of the flat Nesmith spoke to the general with vast relief.

"Well, General, it took nerve to carry that off—but you done it! I've heard of snakes hypnotizing sparrows. I've never heard before of sparrows hypnotizing a mess of snakes!"

"You all behaved admirably," the general said. "Well done, gentlemen."

"But I'm bound to tell you, General—it won't stick. Maybe they'll move onto the reservation. We've given them the best creek, anyway. But what'll keep them there?"

"That occurred to me, Nesmith. As soon as they move in we'll build a fort at the mouth of the creek. We trust them, of course—but the fort will be convenient if they forget the treaty again."

Nesmith was delighted. "It's lucky you didn't mention *that* to Chief Joe!"

"And by the way, Nesmith, what was it you whispered to the interpreter back there? I mean, when they were preparing to shoot us down?"

"I ain't a-going to tell you!" Nesmith chuckled. "It didn't

have anything to do with the treaty. It was just a little remark that Chief Joe understood."

Yes, it was language a Rogue understood. Afterward, on the reservation, Chief Joe talked confidentially to Mox-Mox about the manner in which all his cunning plans had collapsed. The Shastas and the Klamaths had refused to join with them in a general war. Why? Because their scouts, returning from the Table Rock council, reported that the white men were *not* soft; they were mighty warriors. Their chiefs, unarmed, had faced drawn bows and leveled rifles—and laughed.

So now the Rogues were trapped on the reservation. The fort in the lower canyon took care of that. To cap it all, the treaty didn't call for payment to the Rogues in cash, but in merchandise—which couldn't be exchanged for rifles!

"I was a fool, Mox-Mox," Chief Joe admitted with a sigh. "I should have let my warriors kill those white chiefs when they were in my power. . . . It was impossible. How could I signal to my warriors with that smiling chief, Nesmith, sitting beside me? With his hand on his hunting knife inside his shirt?" He spoke sternly. "You have never repeated what he said, Mox-Mox?"

"No, but I have thought of it often." Mox-Mox grinned. "He said, 'You can kill us all, but the first Rogue warrior who falls will be—Chief Joe.'"

"See that your lips remain sealed! . . . No, Mox-Mox, I was mistaken about white men. I was a fox with many tricks and fat with cunning—but *they* were wolves!"

281

GOLDEN INTERLUDE

Legends of lost mines enlivened the talk about many a campfire in the Oregon Country. The search for these lost mines occupied the lives of many men and was responsible for the swift exploration of countless mountain streams and canyons throughout the length of the Cascades Range.

One of the most persistent of such tales had its origin in the high plateau country of eastern Oregon. It seems that the discovery was made by one of the emigrant trains of 1847 as the wagons swung south and west through today's Malheur, Grant, and Crook counties. As to which train found the gold—or where—is a mystery today. That gold was found seems above question. After rich placer ground was opened up at Jacksonville in 1851, hundreds of prospectors crossed the Cascades in search of the lost bonanza. For more than a half century it challenged the imaginations of adventurous men.

The golden tale lives on today, one of the most fascinating of frontier mysteries: the legend of the Blue Bucket Mine.

XXII

THE BLUE BUCKET MINE

T HAT DAY in early fall of 1847 was still and sweltering.
Heat lay in waterless pools on the sage-dotted flats.
Dust pillars stood motionless against the shimmering
horizon. No clouds marred the brazen sky that arched over
the twenty thousand square miles of sand, rimrock, and pine-
clad pinnacles known as the "Oregon High Desert."

Blackbirds wheeled up there in lazy circles. They were
buzzards, and they were watching an emigrant train that
crept like a weary, jointed serpent along a timbered ridge.
No trail extended ahead of the wagons. They had tried
a "short cut" at Fort Hall and now were lost in the high
desert.

Spaced at intervals along the rutted trail behind them
were the bones of cattle and horses; and the buzzards knew
there would be other carcasses to feed upon before *this*
train made it to the Last Mountains.

The wagons descended into a hollow and crossed a shallow
creek. As the last of the train mounted slowly up the bank
through the choking dust the column came to a halt. Something had happened up ahead. Drivers left the gaunt oxen
in charge of the women and went forward to investigate.

In the last wagon was a mother and a little girl, aged
twelve. The little girl's name was Mandy, and she had stood
the dust and heat and thirst pretty well thus far. But when
the wagon stopped and the afternoon sun beat down like

fire on the unprotected slopes she couldn't help thinking about the nice cool creek they had just crossed.

"Maw, can I go back and wade in the creek while we're waiting?"

"Better not, dear. We don't know how long we're going to stop."

"But I'm hot! It isn't far."

"I know. I'd like to do a washing there if we had time." The mother sighed. "We never have time. . . . Now you just wait till we find out, dear. It won't be long."

Word soon came back down the line, shouted from wagon to wagon. Old man Barker, who had been ailing for a week past, had finally died. So the train would stay here the rest of the afternoon while the men dug a decent grave in the rocky soil. After the burying they would push on to the next creek, where there was grass. The creek behind them was too barren for night camp.

So the women in the last dozen wagons decided to do their washing while they waited. There was soon a long line of them descending the hot, dusty slope to the creek. They were barefoot, carrying baskets and buckets. Mandy was in the lead with her blue bucket.

It *had* been blue when they left the Missouri. It was battered and weather-beaten now from being dipped into so many creeks and banged against boulders as it hung from the axletree. Still, it was a good bucket.

When they got to the creek the women tucked up their skirts and rolled up their sleeves and got right out among the boulders, but Mandy led the way upstream.

"Come on, Maw! Look at that nice sand up there!"

"It's quite a ways, dear. We'll have to carry the wet wash all the way back."

"I'll help you! Look—it's in the shade. It's nice and cool."

"Very well, dear."

The sand bar was in the shade because pine trees leaned

286

in from the higher bank. Afterward, many times, they argued about which way the shadows fell across the sand bar. It made a difference, because if the shadow from the pine trees fell across the sand bar from the *far* side, it meant the creek flowed south. If the sun was behind them, the water flowed north. But nobody knew for sure.

At the time Mandy just didn't notice which way the shadows fell. She got to the sand bar first and was soon splashing around in the cool water. It felt good on her bruised, dusty feet. She played in the damp sand while her mother got the washing under way.

"Maw, will we have a creek as nice as this when we get over to the valley?"

"I hope so, dear. If we ever get there."

"This is awfully nice sand," Mandy said. "It's got some pretty rocks in it too. They aren't on top—they're underneath, like little potatoes. Look, they're yellow!"

"Yes, dear."

"Here's one that looks like a peanut! I'm going to keep this one. My, it's heavy! Here—feel it."

"It is heavy, isn't it? No, don't put them in the bucket, honey. I want to carry the clothes in the bucket."

"But they're *clean*. When you wash them off they're as clean as anything. . . . My, there's lots of them. The farther down you dig, the more there are. Just let me take enough to cover the bottom of the bucket, Maw. I want them for my collection."

"Very well, dear."

They carried the wet wash back to the wagon in the blue bucket, whose bottom was covered with pebbles that were dull yellow and very heavy. They spread the clothes on the bushes to dry, and Mandy put the pebbles in her father's tool chest, along with the other rocks she'd picked up on the trail. Then they went up ahead to the funeral, and when it was over the train moved on.

Yes, it made a difference which way the shadows fell across the sand bar, because they never found old man Barker's grave again, nor the trail, nor the creek, though hundreds of men searched for fifty years. The desert sand blew over the grave and blotted out the wagon tracks. The creek looked like dozens of creeks that ran out of the pine timber in the high country.

Meantime, the wagon train crawled on westward, getting farther and farther away from what was probably the richest gold-bearing ground between the Rockies and the Cascades. That's what mining men said afterward when they heard the story.

But the men of the train weren't mining men. None of them had ever seen raw gold. All they were interested in was to get on to the valley.

On the third night after the Barker funeral Mandy's father had some repair work to do. So he opened up his tool chest— and was very much annoyed.

"Mandy!"

"Yes, Daddy?"

"Come over here, young lady! . . . Now look at this! D'ye think we've got nothing to do but haul *rocks* out to Oregon?"

"But I'm making a collection. I'm only keeping the *pretty* rocks!"

"Don't you know," said her father severely, "that the oxen are plumb tuckered out from hauling what we *got* to take along? You throw that junk out while I'm fixing the wagon wheel."

"*Daddy!*"

"Mind now! You're getting to be a regular pack rat. . . . Say, these are funny-looking pebbles, at that! These yellow critters. Where did you find them?"

"Back where we buried old man Barker. They're the prettiest of all! See how heavy they are."

"They feel heavier than lead," her father said curiously. "They look kind of soft too. I'll just pound one out on the wagon tire."

"Not that one, Daddy! That's the one that looks like a peanut. Here—take this one."

"Where's my blacksmith hammer? Here it is. . . . Come along, little Miss Pack Rat."

He pounded out the pebble on the wagon tire, and it really was puzzling. It wasn't as soft as lead, but you could flatten it easily. And it was incredibly tough. You could flatten it as thin as paper and it still hung together. The more you worked it, the prettier it got—a deep yellow, like very rich butter.

The other men of the train gathered around to look at it. Some thought it must be copper. One old-timer, whom they called Uncle Ben, spoke with authority—it was brass! This amused Mandy's father so much that he forgot his annoyance.

"Can I keep them, then? I can, can't I, Daddy?"

"Oh, I guess so. But don't load up with any more of this yellow stuff. It's too doggoned heavy."

The "yellow stuff" was useful ten days later when they camped near a canyon whose bottom was whitened by a roaring river. Some folks thought afterward that it might have been Crooked River, or even the Deschutes. Others said it might have been the John Day.

In any event, they decided to fish in a big pool down in the canyon, so the men and boys got out their fishlines and hooks. So while they were rigging up their lines Mandy saw her father open the toolbox and get out his hammer.

"What you doing, Daddy?"

"We need some sinkers for the fishlines," her father told her. "D'ye mind if I hammer out some of your yellow pebbles?"

"Don't take the one that looks like a peanut! Use the little ones. Now aren't you glad you didn't make me throw them away?"

"You should have picked up more of the stuff, honey. It sure makes good sinkers."

Yes, they weighted their fishlines with virgin gold. They used only the small nuggets, leaving the big ones in the tool chest—the one shaped like a peanut, and the fat ones as big as the first joint of Mandy's thumb, and a dozen or so more that had tiny pits and dents in them, like the eyes of plump little potatoes.

When the train got to the valley finally, after many hardships, the toolbox stayed in the wagon until Mandy's father located some land over in Clackamas County and got the cabin built. Then the toolbox was moved into the woodshed, under the workbench. Mandy looked at her collection of rocks once in a while, but they always looked the same, and when summer came there were too many other things to think about. Finally she forgot all about them.

They stayed in the toolbox, unnoticed and forgotten, until the spring of '51. Mandy's father was gone for a month, fighting the Rogue River Indians, and when he came back he found that a young man named Enright was working on a near-by farm.

This Bill Enright was over to visit practically every evening. He and Mandy seemed to be getting along fine. Mandy's father didn't pay much attention at first, but one evening when he and his wife were sitting on the porch he suddenly grew suspicious.

"Say, what's that Enright critter doing in our woodshed?"

"Sh-h! . . . He's fixing a shovel handle. Bill's a mighty good hand with tools."

"Hasn't he got any tools over to his place? Where's Mandy?"

"She's watching Bill," his wife said, smiling a little.

"What's going on here? What's he hanging around Mandy for?"

"Can't you guess, dear?"

"You mean he's *courting* her? Why, she ain't half grown!"

"You haven't got a very good memory, honey. She's two months older than I was when *we* were married."

"*What?*"

"That's right. She's going on seventeen."

"Hm-m. Where'd this critter come from? Who are his folks?"

"They're back in Maine. . . . Oh, I know all about Bill. He used to be a sailor, and he worked last summer down in the California gold fields. He's going to settle down here as soon as he can find the right farm. He's saved quite a lot of money. He's a good, steady boy."

"A sailor!"

"That was just so he could come out to Oregon. . . . Now don't you get set against him. He's a hard worker, and I'm sure——"

"Oh, he's all right. It's up to Mandy, I reckon. Has he popped the question yet?"

"Sh-h-h!" his wife warned. "I think he's been waiting till you got home. He'll probably be speaking to you about it."

"Good. That shows he's had the right fetching up. . . . Little Mandy! Maw, we're sure getting old!"

Out in the shed Mandy was sitting on the bench, watching young Bill Enright as he expertly shaped the shovel handle. He pretended to be engrossed in his work.

"Well, this looks pretty good, Mandy. I wonder if your dad's got a wood rasp?"

"I'm sure he has. I've seen it around."

"Mandy . . ."

"Yes, Bill?"

"I've been looking at a homestead over on Gales Creek.

The man wants to sell out and move down to the Umpqua. The creek runs right through the place. It's got a nice cabin on it, and a spring."

"I understand that's pretty country over on Gales Creek," Mandy said.

"It sure is. . . . Now *where's* that wood rasp?"

"Maybe it's down there in the tool chest. . . . How far is the cabin from the creek?"

"Right close! The garden patch runs right to the bank." Bill looked at her shyly. "Mandy . . ."

"Yes, Bill?"

"It's quite a ways over to Gales Creek. You've never been away from your folks. I was just wondering——" He broke off, staring into the toolbox. "Well—what's this?"

"Those rocks? Oh, I picked them up when we crossed the high desert. I'd forgotten they were there."

"Let's take them over by the light. . . . Mandy, just where on the high desert did you pick these up?"

"I don't know—in one of the creeks we passed. . . . Bill, it isn't *awfully* far over to Gales Creek."

But he was studying the "yellow stuff." "Don't you know what this is, Mandy? It's *gold.*"

"Gold?"

"I've never seen prettier nuggets! See this one—the one shaped like a peanut? It's worth more than thirty-five dollars!" His excitement increased. "Let's talk to your dad—*he'll* know which creek it was!"

"You mean you want to start hunting for it? Away out there in the desert?"

"I sure do! You'll be rich, Mandy! We'll all be rich!"

"But what about—— Oh, Bill!"

Mandy's father couldn't believe it at first. He laughed at the idea that the yellow pebbles Mandy had gathered in the blue bucket were gold. Then, when Bill finally convinced him, he, too, grew excited.

"Sure we can find that creek! We'll backtrack from The Dalles to where we buried old Barker. I can see that creek plain as day—right there on the north slope below the pine timber!"

"It was a south slope, wasn't it?" his wife asked. "Don't you remember, Mandy, how the shadows fell across the creek?"

"No," Mandy said in a low voice. "I don't remember."

"Why, that was a *north* slope!" her father insisted. "When I was digging old man Barker's grave I kept my back to the sun. That meant I was facing east toward the creek."

"But the ridge was on your left, wasn't it? That would make it a south slope."

"Well, doggone it, there were plenty of other folks with us! We can soon check up. Joe Bemis was there. Let's get right over to Joe Bemis's, Bill——"

"I don't think we'd better talk to anybody, sir," Bill warned. "The thing to do is for the two of us to get over to the high desert—fast. We'd better get some good pack horses and get our outfits lined up——"

"I've got horses! Come on, let's get out to the barn and look them over!"

After they were gone Mandy's mother said with a sigh: "Well, Mandy, that's a man for you! You'd think Paw had had enough hardships in his time without chasing off into the desert. They never grow up! . . . Don't look so blue, honey."

"But Bill was just talking about a beautiful place he'd found over on Gales Creek. He was ready to—— He almost asked me——"

"I know," her mother said. "But don't worry. I haven't talked to Paw yet."

"You mean you can talk Daddy out of it? But how? You didn't say a word against it!"

Her mother smiled a little. "You'll learn how to handle men, honey. Never argue with them while they're excited.

. . . First I'll persuade Paw to wait till the crops are in. There's no great hurry. Nobody else knows the gold's there— so why not wait until after harvest?"

"And then?"

"Then it'll be too late to start till spring, of course!"

"But what about Bill?"

"He can't go without Paw. And as soon as it's good weather we'll all have a picnic over on Gales Creek. When Bill sees you there in that cute little cabin and you tell him what a fine place it is . . . Well, that part of it's up to you, honey!"

"Oh, I hope you're right!"

"And even if they do go next year, or the next, don't worry too much, dear. That's another thing about men. They like to go hunting or fighting Indians or looking for gold—but they soon get tired of it. Outside of something happening to them, there's nothing to worry about. They always come back!"

Yes, Mandy learned about men from her mother. They kept her father and Bill in the valley that year—after that, somehow, they just couldn't get away. Bill talked about it once in a while after he and Mandy were married. Whenever he and Mandy's father got together they'd get excited about it again. They'd draw maps and figure how much of an outfit they'd have to take and how long they'd be gone. But it was always "next summer, *sure*."

Of course the story soon got out. Hundreds of prospectors looked for Mandy's gold. They called it the Blue Bucket Mine. Along in 1862 somebody made a big strike near Powder River and another on Canyon Creek, in the John Day Valley. They were soon working placer ground all through that section. At its peak more than a million a month in nuggets and dust came from Canyon City alone.

One of those gold creeks *might* have been the Blue Bucket Mine. Nobody knew. Mandy didn't care. Neither did Bill as the years went on. He'd tell their sons, "Well, boys, we'd all be millionaires if your mother had just let me go after that gold."

He was only joking, of course. Folks along Gales Creek figured they lived in one of the nicest corners of the continent's richest and most beautiful valley. They felt sorry for the ordinary run of millionaires.

1853

In 1853 came an important milestone in Northwest history. It was the division of the Oregon Territory into two political units, north and south of the Columbia River. The area to the north became Washington Territory, the foundation of a great future state.

The events leading up to that division have more than historic interest. Men shaped the events; and one man in particular—as always at historic crossroads—was ready to take the leadership when the crucial moment arrived.

That man was Michael T. Simmons, a courteous but exceedingly stubborn Kentuckian who crossed the plains with his family in the migration of '44.

In underestimating "Colonel" Simmons's caliber, the Hudson's Bay Company made the final and perhaps most costly of its many mistakes in dealing with that most independent of all history's trail blazers: the wagon-train pioneer.

XXIII

THE COLONEL WAS ANNOYED

BECAUSE Michael T. Simmons was a Kentuckian they called him "Colonel." Because he was also of Irish descent, with a hard-bitten twinkle in his eye on all occasions, he was tremendously popular with his fellow emigrants in the wagon train of '44.

Before the train was many night camps out of Missouri they discovered an interesting and sometimes alarming quirk in the colonel's character. He was easily amused—and even more easily annoyed. Once he was aroused, he had the memory of an elephant and the tenacity of a wolf in dealing with real or imagined wrongs.

The '44 emigrants arrived at Fort Vancouver in the early fall, and Colonel Simmons went up to the fort to discuss the matter of provisions for his impoverished family and friends. This was before the settling of the boundary dispute, and the Hudson's Bay Company still dominated the Columbia.

Unfortunately for the Company and the British Empire, Dr. McLoughlin happened to be down-river on business that day. He had left the fort in charge of his dour chief clerk, Alexander McLeod; and McLeod, a good clerk, was no McLoughlin when it came to dealing with short-tempered American settlers.

McLeod made the fatal mistake of patronizing the tall, quiet-mannered Kentuckian.

"You don't have to explain, Simmons—I know what you're after. You and your party have arrived here ragged and hungry, as usual. You want to buy supplies. Is that it?"

"That's correct, suh."

"And you've no money, of course?"

Simmons's pale blue eyes examined McLeod with kindling interest. "We're not beggars, suh. I'll work to pay the bill."

"Work? What work can you do? Can you split shingles?"

"Yes, suh."

"Very well. I'll give you an order on our storekeeper. Let me have your list." McLeod studied the list, muttering, "You Yankees! You're the most improvident people! And why come out here in such numbers? . . . You'll be settling in the valley, I suppose?"

"We haven't decided, suh. We've been thinking of looking over the Rogue River in the spring. We don't know anything about the country up north."

"Oh, you'll go south," McLeod said in an offhand way. "You can't settle north of the Columbia. . . . Well, here's your list, Simmons. I've approved it. Just hand it to the storekeeper. And mind you show up in the morning!"

"You may depend on me, suh." Simmons took the list and folded it thoughtfully. "Did I understand you to say, Mr. McLeod, that we *can't* settle north of the Columbia? Why not?"

"Because the Hudson's Bay Company doesn't approve of it!"

"Isn't the Joint Occupation Treaty still in force?"

"Yes, yes, but you must abide by the wishes of the Hudson's Bay. We've no objection to your settling anywhere in the south. . . . Now don't tell me, Simmons, that you're suddenly interested in going *north*?"

"You've made it sound mighty interesting, suh," the colonel admitted. "I'll tell you later—after I get the shingles split."

McLeod's manner changed the course of the Northwest's history. The colonel was annoyed. Moreover, his patriotism was aroused. Just *who* was the Hudson's Bay Company—a British concern—to say that freeborn Americans couldn't settle where they pleased in the Oregon Country?

So Simmons kept his party on the north bank of the Columbia. They comprised a dozen families, ready to go wherever the colonel led. They moved in for the winter at the mouth of the Cowlitz, and Simmons cut shingles at Fort Vancouver. He did no secret spying. He asked questions openly—and kept his ears open.

In midwinter, when his shingles were all split, he had another exchange with McLeod. This time McLeod was on guard. The doctor had warned him that he must try to undo the harm he had done. For the doctor himself to attempt it would merely feed Simmons's suspicions.

McLeod did his best. He had now adopted an ingratiating manner.

"Well, Mr. Simmons, your account is settled. . . . It's *Colonel* Simmons, isn't it?"

"*Mister* Simmons is sufficient, suh."

"You've done your work in a very satisfactory manner. We'll be happy to extend you more credit if necessary."

"Thank you. We're in pretty good shape now. We're greatly obliged to the Hudson's Bay."

"Quite all right. . . . By the way, where have you decided you'll locate?"

"We're going to explore up north, toward the Puget Sound country." The colonel eyed him fixedly. "Any objections, suh?"

"Not at all! You misunderstood me on that point last fall. What I meant was, the Company *advised* against it. In your own interest, you understand. There's no good farm land up there. The country's rough. The Indians are hostile."

"Isn't the Hudson's Bay operating a large farm on the Nisqually?"

"That's true—and we have *all* the good land. We have the protection of our fort up there. But it's no place for settlers. Our best advice to you, Mr. Simmons, is to settle in the valley."

301

"Let's be honest with each other, suh. Isn't it true that the British are preparing to claim everything north of the Columbia? On the pretext that there are no American settlers up there?"

"Really, Simmons, that's an international question. Isn't it outside our province——"

"Very well, suh. We won't debate it." The colonel's hard eyes twinkled. "But let me thank the Company again, Mr. McLeod. Particularly for its good *advice*."

No, it was too late for McLeod's attempt at diplomacy. He had unchained a force that was like a stream in the mountains. Continental barriers might oppose it, but sooner or later it would reach the sea.

When summer came the colonel led a party of men north to Puget Sound. He explored the southern end of the sound by canoe and was delighted with what he saw. He knew he was looking upon one of the world's finest inland waterways.

He took up a claim on the banks of the Deschutes River, near a waterfall that tumbled down toward Budd Inlet. He called this spot Newmarket, later changing it to Tumwater, as it appears on the maps today. He and his party returned for their families that fall and took them north. Other settlers followed in the spring and located on Whidby Island, at the present sites of Seattle, Olympia, and Centralia, and at various points in the Cowlitz Valley.

The influx came just in time. The British could no longer claim exclusive settlement north of the Columbia. The treaty of 1846 moved the international boundary more than two hundred and fifty miles northward—at the forty-ninth parallel of latitude.

The American flag now waved over the Oregon Country. The Hudson's Bay Company still held their land along the north bank of the Nisqually, and Colonel Simmons watched them like a hawk. The river of his annoyance had not yet reached the sea.

He soon uncovered a foul plot and called the first public meeting held by American citizens in the Puget Sound area.

"Gentlemen," he announced, having assumed the chairmanship as a matter of course, "the Hudson's Bay Company have moved some cattle across the Nisqually and are spreading out along the south bank. It's plain enough what they're up to. It's skulduggery, gentlemen! Under the treaty they're to be paid for all the land they occupy—so they're trying to occupy more land! We must put a stop to this immediately! . . . If there's no objection I'll appoint a committee to serve notice on them to move their cattle back across the river. Hearing no objection, it is so ordered!"

The head of the committee which framed and delivered the ultimatum to the Hudson's Bay Company was—Colonel Simmons. This time Company officials properly appraised the cold twinkle in the colonel's pale blue eyes. Within the week all Company cattle were returned across the river to the north bank. . . . Years later, before an international commission, the Hudson's Bay Company claimed their Nisqually holdings to be worth three million dollars. They received less than one fourth that amount.

With affairs of state settled for the moment, the colonel prospered at Tumwater. In 1849 he sold his holdings there for thirty-five thousand dollars, invested this in a ship, loaded it with Douglas-fir spars, and sent it to San Francisco. He seemed on his way to becoming a wealthy man. But a trusted partner absconded with all his capital in San Francisco and left him practically bankrupt.

This annoyed the colonel but didn't dishearten him. At Smithfield—later known as Olympia—he had started the first American store on Puget Sound. It was a community gathering place, a hotbed of political discussion. The voice that soon led all the others, with mounting irritation, was that of Colonel Simmons. He was in the thick of a new crusade.

"Gentlemen, *we* built this country north of the Columbia.

We're capable of running our own affairs. Why should we travel two hundred miles to lay our problems before a territorial legislature made up of settlers of the Willamette Valley? *I* say—let's organize a new territory. If they oppose us we'll fight them to a finish! Why should those valley men who have never seen the Olympics, nor the timbered shores of Puget Sound . . ."

The colonel could expand this theme for hours.

This was in 1851; and a Fourth of July oration at Olympia, delivered by a young and zealous attorney named Chapman, added fuel to the patriotic fires the colonel had kindled. A preliminary meeting was held in August, and on October 25 of the following year, 1852, a formal convention assembled at Monticello, near the mouth of the Cowlitz. Forty-four delegates attended, including eight from the growing village of Seattle.

Colonel Simmons refused any office in the convention. He preferred to observe from the side lines; and the object of his smiling but ominous scrutiny was the representative of the Oregon Legislature, sent up to listen and report.

Through all the preliminaries this valley delegate sat attentive and silent—and the colonel grew more and more annoyed. In this valley man's composure the colonel saw a touch of sinister complacence—as though the smug Oregonian knew, and was secretly amused at the knowledge, that all this was the merest horseplay unless the valley approved it. Valley settlers outnumbered those north of the river by eight to one.

Finally a Puget Sound delegate sitting next to the colonel asked him cautiously when the "fireworks" would begin. Everyone knew the colonel was, in frontier terminology, "loaded for bear."

"Let him declare himself, suh!" the colonel replied. "We've fought the Hudson's Bay. We've fought the Indians. We certainly won't take insult or dictation from these valley men!

Just let him state how the valley wants to fight and on what grounds, and we shall certainly oblige him!"

Finally the moment came. The convention adopted a memorial to Congress asking for the creation of a new territory. The chairman then asked the valley delegate to state what the attitude of the valley would be toward this division of Oregon Territory.

The Oregon man replied—and the most astounded man in Monticello was Colonel Michael T. Simmons.

"Gentlemen of the convention, the people of the valley congratulate you. We have always felt that the Columbia was our natural northern boundary. Above that boundary you gentlemen have created what shall certainly be a great commonwealth—and you have our hearty support in this first major step!"

The delegates cheered wildly. The Oregon man continued:

"Our legislature meets next November, and I am sure I can promise you that we, too, shall adopt a memorial to Congress along the same lines. Our delegate in Congress, General Lane, will work actively for it. . . . Our interests are mutual, gentlemen! Though a political boundary may one day separate us, we shall continue to face the future as one, undivided!"

The colonel was caught completely flat-footed. He had expected—and certainly not with distaste—a battle royal. He had prowled the convention like a hopeful old wolf, hackles up and fire in his eye—and here was no enemy, but a dove of peace! He couldn't believe it, in fact, until the Oregon Legislature met in November and the Oregonians did adopt the memorial and instructed General Lane, in Washington, to get quick action on it.

The colonel often chuckled over that Monticello business when discussing it with cronies up in his Puget Sound store.

"Well, suhs," he told them, "I learned a lesson from that valley man. There I sat, full of vinegar and brimstone, hating the sight of him. I didn't like the shape of his nose or the way he parted his hair. No honest citizen, I told myself, *ever* had ears like that! . . . Then he began to speak, and he changed by the minute. When he was through I was proud to shake his hand. He was a gentleman, suhs, and a right handsome lad!"

Congress acted quickly on the memorials. The next spring —in March 1853—the bill creating the new territory became law. The settlers had suggested the name Columbia, but this was changed during the debate to Washington Territory to avoid confusion with the District of Columbia. This made no difference out along the Cowlitz and up in Puget Sound. The great goal had been achieved!

And almost immediately Colonel Simmons walked in the shadow of a new worry. He wasn't annoyed—yet. But a gleam was kindling in his eye. President Pierce had appointed Isaac I. Stevens as first governor of Washington Territory.

Who was this Stevens? Rumor indicated that he might be a stiff-necked, military, pompous character. He was from Massachusetts. He had been educated at West Point. He was not only coming out as governor but also as head of a railroad survey party *and* as Superintendent of Indian Affairs.

All this filled the colonel with mounting concern.

"I ask you, suhs, what kind of meat has this man Stevens been eating? Is being governor of this territory so picayune a job that he must also undertake a railroad survey? *Besides* taking care of all the Indians in his spare time? And I've been unfortunate enough to meet some folks from Boston. They look down their noses at men whose hands are callused from honest labor. Gentlemen, *Mister* Stevens may find this is a very rough community!"

Actually—as the colonel was soon to discover—President Pierce had made an excellent appointment. Governor Stevens was neither stiff-necked nor officious. Though his appearance was mild he was of outstanding caliber, intellect, and resolution. Like General Joseph Lane, first governor of Oregon Territory, he was to become one of the historic figures of the Northwest.

Stevens brought his large engineering party westward, surveying as he advanced. He crossed the Rockies in early fall and made treaties with the untamed Yakimas as he moved down toward the Columbia. He was a master treaty maker—and a grim avenger when those treacherous interior tribes, mistaking his courteous manner for softness, later broke the treaties. He reached the lower Columbia and was entertained at Fort Vancouver—now a United States Army post.

Then, pushing ahead of his party, he arrived alone and unannounced in the frontier village on Budd Inlet called Olympia. That fact set the stage for his dramatic—and amusing—introduction to his official duties on the nation's farthest frontier.

For the young and quiet-mannered governor was not only alone and unescorted; he was ragged, unkempt, weary, and hungry. He located an establishment which appeared to be a public eating place—and was not cordially received.

"No, we ain't selling any meals today, mister. There's big doings coming off here pretty soon. We got to get ready for it."

"But I'm hungry, man!" Stevens protested. "I've come a long ways today."

"Can't help it! We've got no time, I tell you!"

"Then let me get out to the kitchen. I'll eat scraps. I'll promise not to get in the way."

"Well—all right. See that you don't get underfoot!"

So the new governor of Washington Territory—reared in Boston, educated at West Point, a hero of the Mexican War —stood in the rough, noisy kitchen, kept out of the way of sweating cooks, and ate odds and ends of meat, fish, potatoes, and bread until his hunger was satisfied.

Then he went out on the street, well fed and cheerful, and found the village crowded with frontiersmen. He approached a tall, dignified citizen and spoke to him courteously.

"I've just arrived here, sir. May I ask—what's all the excitement?"

The citizen fixed pale blue, twinkling eyes upon him. "You *are* a stranger, young man! There's going to be a big banquet. We're expecting the *Honorable* Isaac I. Stevens, the new governor of Washington Territory."

"Really? Then I'm your man, I suppose. I'm Stevens."

"You!"

"Yes. I came ahead of the party—perhaps I shouldn't have been so informal. I didn't expect a Roman holiday."

"You mean, Governor, you figured you weren't entitled to all this fuss and feathers?"

"Naturally not," Stevens said smilingly. "I'll be delighted to meet the people, of course. I'll need friends—plenty of them—to help me do a good job."

"Suh," said his companion, his bleak face softening, "I am Colonel Michael T. Simmons. Permit me to shake your hand. Welcome to Olympia, suh!" Then he turned and shouted to a near-by group of men: "Sound the alarm! Tell the boys to get the food on the table! The governor's here!"

There was a circular saw hanging from a post. A man beat upon it with an iron bar, and the town came running. By the time the banquet was served—though the governor ate without appetite, being full of kitchen scraps—he and the colonel were fast friends.

Stevens's modesty was at odds with his record in the Mexican War. His youth was belied by the fact that he had led a party of 254 men across the continent—through the country of the treacherous Sioux and across the Rockies—and had lost not a man. Beneath his courteous manner the colonel recognized a person of force.

And Simmons's approval warmed the crowd, so that when

the governor rose to speak he no longer faced a truculent and critical audience but men disposed to be neighbors and friends. The governor felt this and reacted to it, and the knowledge added confidence to his quiet sincerity of manner.

Down the long table a man whispered jokingly to the colonel, reminding him that this was the stiff-necked Bostonian for whom the colonel had promised a rough reception. But the colonel was in no mood for frivolity.

"Where a man's born is an accident of geography," he said severely. "He's a Kentuckian at heart. . . . Quiet, suh! The governor of Washington Territory's about to speak."

Stevens's simple words permeated the farthest corners of the rough hall:

"Gentlemen of Washington Territory, I am not here to govern but to aid you to govern yourselves. My part will be small until I have learned your problems—and I will then need your advice and assistance in meeting and mastering them. And master them we shall, gentlemen, whatever they may be! . . . I consider it a privilege as well as a high honor . . ."

The governor had already gained his first and most important victory. Without it, he might have met defeat as an administrator. With it—in the year 1853, in Washington Territory—he could not fail. It was like gaining the strength of a great river, a force disdainful of mountains or men. It was:

"Suh, I am Colonel Michael T. Simmons. At your service, Governor. . . ."

1843 – 1859

The rapidity with which the Oregon Country developed is one of the phenomena of world history.

Only one hundred and two men voted at Champoeg in 1843. The nation's frontier was eighteen hundred miles eastward, and between that frontier and Champoeg were the trackless plains and the Continental Divide.

Three years later a deep-rutted wagon trail spanned the continent. That year—1846—title to the entire Oregon Country passed peacefully to the United States; and in 1848, only five years after Champoeg, Oregon was a territory—self-made, self-supporting, self-governed. No other global frontier had been tamed so quickly.

And by 1856, just thirteen years after Champoeg, the Oregon Territory was ready for its final step as a political entity—statehood. The events of the years 1856–59 rang down the curtain on the nation's most colorful frontier drama—the saga of the Oregon pioneer.

XXIV

TRAIL'S END

THE social evolution of man has produced no more rugged individualist than the Oregon pioneer. He defied Indians, deserts, starvation, and death on his westward march. He needed no military force to precede him; he was himself a conqueror. Once on the ground, he needed no federal "authority" to tell him where to plow, what crops he could raise, or when. Today's talk about "the underprivileged," "managed economy," and "cradle-to-the-grave security" would have filled him with ludicrous amazement. He created his own privileges, managed his own economy, defended his security—and died free.

The Oregon pioneer loved a good joke, but in matters of government he kept his feet on the ground. Government affected his personal freedom, and this he yielded grudgingly. This elemental viewpoint made him one of the nation's most astute thinkers on public affairs. He had scanned too many thickets for hostile Indians—and had guarded his hen house against too many prowling skunks—to be taken in by insincerity or double talk.

Ambitious and "clever" politicians soon learned this to their sorrow. The Willamette Valley was one of the nation's most beautiful and productive regions, but for glittering phrases and campaign oratory it was rough and stony ground.

A typical settler's reaction to the bombast of the day was somewhat as follows:

"Well, sir, that was a fine speech! I enjoyed every minute of it. Did you ever see a man pound the table harder or wave his arms faster? It was like he was fighting a swarm of bees. Of course he didn't *say* anything. There was plenty of chaff —but doggoned little wheat!"

The politicians learned the hard way. As early as 1853 they decided the time had come for Oregon to acquire the dignity of statehood. They made much of the word "dignity" and such phrases as "joining the community of states" and "adding another star to the nation's flag." They submitted the question to the people in '54 and prepared for happy days at Salem. Statehood meant a whole constellation of new political offices, new state buildings, and new taxes.

But down in old Yamhill and Polk counties, and along the Chehalem, and over on the Tualatin Plains, the settlers searched all this chaff and found little wheat. These were men who had forded icy rivers, slept in waterless deserts, and buried their own dead.

"Ain't the boys getting a little ambitious down there at Salem? We're making out all right. We've got our own man as governor now, and our own Supreme Court. How many of these politicians have we got to support? Who pays the bills? No, sir, I'm agin it!"

The 1854 measure lost by more than a thousand votes. The politicians were staggered at this backwoods viewpoint. The people just didn't understand. They were denying themselves the privileges of a great commonwealth.

It appeared that the people did understand: in 1855 they voted it down again. In 1856 it was submitted a third time, and for the third time it lost.

Meanwhile, the settlers had fought the Indian wars. They had large claims against the Federal Government for costs and property damage sustained in these wars. The fact that a state had representatives who could vote in Congress, while a territorial delegate had no vote at all, was an argument

314

outweighing all the glittering oratory that had gone before. *This* made sense.

"Well, it looks like we're driven into this state business. When it comes to taxes and politicians we're going to be as bad off as a bobtailed bull in fly time. But how are we going to collect what's coming to us if our man back in Washington can only sit there and twiddle his thumbs when the voting starts? . . . Yep, we might as well take a big breath and jump into the creek."

Thus in 1857 the people voted more than four to one to hold a state constitutional convention.

The politicians were overjoyed. At last the people were committed. The rest would be easy—hold a convention, adopt a constitution, then apply for admission as a state. Drawing up a constitution would be a delightful chore in which the people would have no part. It would include the creation of state offices *and* attendant salaries. Happy days were here at last!

Their triumph became tinged with alarm when the final returns came in. The people had elected delegates to the convention, and many of these delegates were *not* professional politicians. They were jovial, hardheaded, hard-bitten valley men—like Frederick Waymire of Polk County. The moment Waymire took the floor at the convention and made his first speech the other farm delegates all sat back with a sigh of relief. They had found a leader.

The professionals listened to Waymire with amusement. Waymire *was* amusing—but his humor had the quality of the emigrant trail. It was the humor of strong men who face deserts and death smilingly and to whom a spade is always a spade.

"Mr. Chairman," Waymire announced, "I'm Fred Waymire of Polk County. Gentlemen of the convention, I've only got one eye, as you've probably noticed. But it's a *good* eye. It can spot a rascal a long ways off—and it can see straight ahead in the line of duty. . . . And this is the line I'm look-ing down right now, folks. I'm agin high salaries, high taxes, and slavery. Also, I aim to see that this state's a mighty un-healthy place for crooked corporations."

He was immediately challenged. A cultured voice shouted:

"Mr. Chairman, I would like to ask Mr. Waymire a ques-tion on the subject of corporations. . . . Mr. Waymire, have you had any experience with corporations?"

"I sure have! And, brother, I'll never forget it!"

"Has the gentleman from Polk County ever owned stock in a corporation?"

"Have I owned stock in a corporation, he says!" Waymire was aghast. "Have I owned stock— Listen, folks. Get holt of yourselves and hang on while I tell you what a corporation done to me over in Polk County. . . . It was maybe three-four years ago when one of these city dudes kind of eased up to me, with his hair all slicked back and his mouth full of beautiful teeth. . . ."

Many of Waymire's listeners had heard the story. The pro-fessional politicians had not, and they settled themselves to listen with benevolent amusement. They were unaware that they were listening to words that were molding history; that the voice of Frederick Waymire was the voice of the rulers of Oregon.

It seemed that Waymire was plowing that day and was resting his team beside the road at the unfortunate moment when the city "slicker" drove up in his spanking new surrey. In Waymire's eyes—so Waymire insisted—this stranger was a model of elegance and culture; and he was greatly flattered when the stranger pulled up and addressed him affably.

"Hello, there! You're Fred Waymire, aren't you?"

"That's right. But where have I met up with you before?"

"You haven't. But you'll know me from now on, I think. Mr. Waymire, my name's Johnson. I represent the Alta California Telegraph Company."

"Howdy."

"Do you know what we're going to do, Waymire?" The stranger fairly glowed with enthusiasm. "We're organizing a corporation to build and operate a telegraph line from Portland to San Francisco. You know what a telegraph line is?"

"Oh, shore—a feller told me how it works. It's something like a dog with a long tail."

"A dog with a long tail?"

"That's the way I heard it. Suppose this dog's tail is long enough to stretch from Portland to San Francisco. You twist his tail in Portland and this hound yelps in San Francisco."

"Very good!" the stranger applauded. "Very amusing! Mr. Waymire, we're going to build this line right through Yamhill and Polk counties. We'll start from Portland with a crew of men——"

"Hold on a second! Who's doing all this?"

"Why, you are. And all the other responsible citizens of the valley."

"I thought you said the corporation was going to do it?" Waymire objected.

"Certainly. But everybody will buy stock. It's the opportunity of a lifetime. As soon as we've sold enough of this stock——"

"Nope," Waymire cut in. "I got all the stock I can handle. The place is plumb cluttered up with cows and heifers and hogs. If I was to buy one more potbellied shoat——"

"No, no—stock in the corporation! Not *livestock!* . . . Listen. This is how the corporation is set up. First a group of us get together . . ."

Waymire listened——so Waymire asserted—with tremendous interest. This corporation business sounded like quite a neighborly enterprise. Instead of getting together for a barn raising, or to thresh some wheat, they just pooled their money and called it a corporation. Each stockholder had a vote. If they didn't like the way the corporation was doing business they could get together and vote on it. It was just like running the government!

"And the funny thing is, folks, that I didn't stop to ask—and neither did my neighbors—what the Sam Hill us farmers down in Polk County would do with a *telegraph* line! It was about as useful to us as ears on a grub hoe. No, sir, we were plumb bedazzled by this corporation idea. And right after that the grief began. The corporation built this line and strung up those beautiful wires. . . ."

Yes, there was plenty of grief. The line never went farther than Corvallis, and it was very expensive to build. So the stockholders put up more money. This was called an "assessment."

Then came the great day when the first message sputtered over the wires. They twisted the tail in Portland and the hound yelped in Corvallis. Then they twisted it in Corvallis and it yelped in Portland. It was practically a miracle. But after that . . .

Well, after that the posts just stood there and gathered moss, and the crows came and roosted on the sagging wires. It developed that the wires weren't paid for, nor all the costs of labor. So creditors gathered like wolves and roamed the highways and byways of Polk County and beat a path to the door of—Frederick Waymire.

"And I said to these creditors: 'Folks, you know Fred Waymire. He's an honest man. He pays his debts. But this here's the *corporation's* debts. . . . Now you just hunt up the officers of this said corporation. Tell 'em Fred Waymire says to treat you right and pay you every dime you got coming.'"

Unfortunately the officers of the corporation—the promoters—had already left for parts unknown. They had taken the corporation's cash with them. And Fred Waymire discovered, to his astonishment and horror, that he and his friends were the corporation, responsible for the corporation's debts.

Waymire didn't believe it. He had paid for the stock. He

victed. . . .' Yep, that's fair enough. We started free. We stay free."

On November 9, 1857, the people spoke. The constitution was adopted by a majority of approximately two to one, and slavery was rejected by three to one. Another section voted on, later nullified, excluded free slaves and mulattoes.

Ratification by Congress came more than a year later. The free-state clause brought bitter opposition from the South. The fires of the Civil War were smoldering now, ready to burst into flame. But the Oregon Admission Bill was finally passed by the Senate and House and approved by the President on February 14, 1859.

The news didn't reach San Francisco until March 10. It arrived by steamer at Oregon City on March 15—and an Oregon City youth named Stephen Senter was suddenly inflamed by the drama of it. This was a historic moment! They hadn't heard about it down at Salem! Why not saddle his horse and ride to the capital like a second Paul Revere, shouting his news to the countryside?

So Senter started out through mud and rain, thundering toward Salem. Folks could hear him coming a mile away, and they rushed out to get a look at him and find out what he was yelling about.

"Oregon's a state!" Senter shouted, galloping by. "The President's signed the bill! Hurrah for Oregon!"

But Senter was a newcomer in the valley. He didn't know his Oregon. After he'd gone by the uproar died in the distance; neighbors looked at each other and shook their heads.

"So Oregon's a state, eh? Hm-m. Well, well! . . . Say, what ailed that lad? He's liable to run his horse plumb into the ground. Excitable critter, wasn't he?"

When Senter finally reached Salem, exhausted, his news was calmly received. The newly elected state officeholders had been waiting for word for a month past, but the public generally was undisturbed. There was some talk about firing a dozen cannon by way of celebration. But it was raining, and there wasn't much of a crowd, so they compromised on one cannon and fired one shot.

That cannon shot marked the end of a cycle which had begun when Captain Robert Gray ventured across the bar of the Columbia in 1792. The first settlers' meetings, the Provisional Government, the Territorial Government—these had served their separate purposes on the nation's last frontier. Now, in 1859, it was the *state* of Oregon, a commonwealth within a commonwealth which spanned the world's richest continent.

Yet the people of Oregon were unchanged. Talk about the "benefits" and "privileges" of statehood left them unimpressed. They had fought for their own benefits, created their own privileges. Statehood was the natural and final machinery of self-government, self-imposed by a free people. Therefore, it was, and properly so, merely a historic milestone which loomed up beside the path of empire, along the march of conquerors, and moved on as casually, without fanfare, into the mighty panorama of the past.

OLD SONG AND STORY

Shortly after the Hudson's Bay Company was established at Fort Vancouver, in 1825, white men had the leisure to study one of the natural wonders of the continent—the Columbia gorge, where the great river had plowed a thirty-mile cleft directly through the heart of the Cascades Range.

It was a scene of grandeur, of magnificent dimensions. All about—on crumbling slopes and towering cliffs—were evidences of titanic struggle when the world was young.

At one point in the gorge were the imposing ruins marking the greatest battle of all—where the irresistible river had come into head-on collision with the very backbone of the continent. Giant scars were still fresh on the mighty slopes. The river was still choked with debris. . . . What towering structure had once joined wall to wall? Why and when had it fallen? What thunders had accompanied it when the very foundations of the mountains had at last given way and all that incalculable mass had crashed into the gorge?

The Indians knew. It had been an event so enormous, so literally earth-shaking, that none of the storytellers of any of the tribes could explain it in human terms. It must be told through the deeds of the Powerful Ones, the Watchers, the Spirit-Chiefs who lived far above the snow fields of the highest peaks. . . . Thus originated the great saga of the Columbia—the legend of the Bridge of the Gods.

XXV

THE BRIDGE OF THE GODS*

IN THOSE days (so the Old Ones say) a messenger came to
the Spirit-Chief, Tyee, and said: "Down by the river,
above the great bridge, there is one who weeps." So Tyee
left his place in the mountains and went down and walked
among his people.

It was the time of the spring salmon, which is a very pleasant time beside the river. Tyee had been good, and the
people were busy and happy. There was much shouting and
laughter. The spears of the warriors were flashing in the
rapids. The young squaws were carrying the salmon up the
bank. The old squaws were splitting the fish and spreading
them out to dry in the sun. Children played in the warm sand.
. . . Where was the one who wept?

Then Tyee saw an old woman sitting alone on a point of
rock. He went and stood beside her. When she saw that it
was Tyee she tried to wipe the tears from her eyes. But new
tears came, so she looked up steadfastly at Tyee, her black
eyes glittering. . . . Her name was Loo-et, which is a beautiful name, meaning "little one." But Loo-et was toothless
and withered and very ugly.

*Though some scientists disagree, a majority of the geologists who have
studied the terrain are of the opinion that a great natural bridge once spanned
the Columbia gorge. It is a striking fact that all Indian tribes of the locality,
without exception, assert through their legends that such a bridge stood for
ages at the indicated site and collapsed perhaps a century before the white
man came. Each tribe had its own explanation of the origin and fall of the
great bridge. Reproduced here is one of the most beautiful of the Klickitat
versions.

"Why are *you* not busy, Loo-et?" Tyee asked. "Where is your lodge?"

"I have no lodge," Loo-et replied. "My warrior and my sons are gone. My daughters live in the lodges of distant tribes."

"You are sad because you are lonely and old and death is close? Well, it is the way of life."

"I do not fear loneliness or death. There is no baby for me to watch. There is no fire to tend. No one needs Loo-et. . . . That is all, Tyee. It is of no importance."

But the reply pleased Tyee. She was a woman of character. So Tyee looked about him at the many happy lodges. He looked beyond the bridge, down-river, where the people from the west were also in camp on the salmon grounds. There was no place for Loo-et. So he looked up thoughtfully at the bridge.

It was a *great* bridge—so high that the trees growing along its level top seemed as small as ferns. Even its underside, which was like the roof of a big cave, was so high that the birds nesting there were tiny as moths. None but warriors passed under the bridge, and only in time of war, because great rocks fell there day and night, rumbling and thundering as in a dark cavern.

Yet it was a beautiful bridge, and useful. Tyee had built it so that all the people, and the gods themselves when they walked with men, could cross the river in safety from the north and south.

"I have decided how you can be useful, Loo-et," Tyee said at last. "The people use fire, but they cannot make fire. When the ashes grow cold they must borrow new coals from the nearest lodge, but sometimes the nearest lodge is far away. So this is your task. Up on the great bridge you will keep a fire burning—in winter and summer, in sunlight and storm—so that those who need coals will come to you. . . . There—is that not good, Loo-et?"

326

"It is good! I will keep the fire burning! . . . But wait, I am very old. The people will learn to depend on me, and then the time will come when I must join my warrior. . . ."

"No, you will not die, Loo-et." Tyee smiled benevolently. "I am making you immortal."

X So Loo-et's fire shone on the great bridge day and night. By day its smoke could be seen far up and down the river. By night it was a star hanging in the sky. Many borrowed coals from Loo-et. The squaws said that Loo-et's fire heated the stones faster and there was less smoke in the lodge.

But one day a messenger came to Tyee and said: "Loo-et is weeping."

So Tyee went down to the bridge, and Loo-et looked up at him, her dark eyes glistening with tears.

"I am ashamed, Tyee. Pay no attention to me. It is nothing. I am useful and happy."

"Then why do you weep?".

"Because I am a woman and very foolish. . . . It is this, Tyee. When the squaws come to borrow my fire they look at me and shake their heads. They are thinking, 'I am not as old and ugly as Loo-et.' Even the blind ones—the oldest of all, the ones with the crooked hands—say to their children: 'Tell me again how ugly Loo-et is.' And the warriors turn their faces away and hurry by. . . . I am so *very* ugly, Tyee."

"You have already forgotten, then, that all you wanted was to be useful?"

"You are immortal, Tyee," Loo-et said humbly, "so you do not know how mortal men and women welcome death when they grow old. It is good to be useful, yes, but it is only while waiting in the twilight for night to come. But *I* will never see the light. I will never see my warrior or my sons in Spirit-Land. They will never say: 'Ah—Loo-et has come at last. *Now* the food will be cooked and the salmon dried and our lodge will never grow cold.'"

"And so?"

"If—if you could only make me beautiful . . . I do not want the warriors to notice me," Loo-et went on hurriedly, "nor to make the other squaws envious. It is only that I must always wait in the twilight, alone by my fire. Forever is a long time when one is so *very* ugly. . . . I do not complain, of course. I am useful. The fire must be kept burning."

"What you are asking for means much trouble," Tyee said. "Still, you have faithfully tended your fire. . . . I can change your body, Loo-et. But your heart will still be old. Even Tyee cannot bring back the yesterdays that are long since gone."

"I do not ask to be young at heart," Loo-et said eagerly. "I will not encourage warriors to sit by my fire—if they will only smile at me cheerfully when they pass by! If the squaws will not pity me! If the little children will not shrink away when I touch their hands! . . . Make me beautiful, Tyee."

So Tyee, though his wisdom warned against it, made her beautiful.

Now Loo-et's dark eyes sparkled, and her dark braids hung glistening over her bosom, and her rounded cheeks held the bloom of wild roses. The fame of her beauty soon spread up and down the river and north and south in the mountains. Though Loo-et did not encourage them, old warriors often paused beside her fire, pretending they had stopped only to warm their hands. Young warriors lingered there. Squaws looked at her and whispered enviously: "No good will come of this."

And presently, as Tyee had feared, the big trouble came. The fame of Loo-et's beauty spread south into the mountains and finally reached mighty Wy-east, the young and proud chief who ruled all of the country south of the river. Wy-east was Tyee's younger son and was of calm and noble countenance, though his rage was terrible when fully aroused.

Tyee's elder son, Klickitat, ruled all of the country north of the river. Klickitat was of bold and savage temper, gifted

328

with the use of words which enraged Wy-east, so that they had always fought each other. For this reason Tyee had forbidden both to cross the river. Each must stay on his own side.

But Loo-et's fire was in the center of the bridge—and one night when the shadows were deep in the canyon but the high summer moon was shining on the bridge, Loo-et looked up and saw a young, tall, and stately warrior standing by her fire, leaning on his war club. He was smiling, and for a moment Loo-et forgot that she was old at heart and smiled back, her smooth cheeks dimpling.

Then she remembered, and terror made her heart beat wildly.

"No—don't come closer! Who are you?"

"I am Wy-east. Don't be afraid, Loo-et. I won't eat you, little one, even if you *are* prettier than a wild strawberry."

"Go quickly, Wy-east," Loo-et pleaded. "Remember Tyee's command. You shouldn't leave your bank of the river."

Wy-east laughed. "But I haven't *crossed* the river. . . . Listen, Loo-et. I have a message for you. I have carried it in my heart these many years. I have dreamed it many times in my empty lodge in the lonely nights. . . ."

"No, no—I mustn't listen! I honor you, Wy-east, but I must tend my fire. Please——"

"Hush!" Wy-east said gently. "You are beautiful, Loo-et. They told me and I didn't believe them——"

A harsh voice spoke from the shadows: "And your appearance, my dear brother, is strangely like that of a sick rabbit leaning against a hot rock."

"Klickitat!" Loo-et cried, terrified.

"Yes, my dear." Klickitat came into the circle of firelight, his war club in his hand, and looked disdainfully at Wy-east. "Come, Loo-et, let *that* squaw tend the fire. I have a lodge in the mountains—a beautiful lodge. You will enjoy it. Come, little one!"

"Don't touch me! Both of you must go—quickly!"

Wy-east's voice rose in anger. "Take your hand from the maiden's arm, Klickitat!"

"Ah," Klickitat said, "that *is* a war club you have there? Do you know how to use it? Good. Let us move away from the fire, dear brother. . . ."

"No, no—stop! Please don't fight!"

"Stop!" a distant voice shouted. "I am a messenger from Tyee!"

It was too late. No one but Tyee himself could stop them now. Tyee was coming fast, calling on the wind to give him speed—but too late.

The sound of the battle swelled on the river and rolled louder and louder through the mountains. Warriors came running from east and west and north and south, but they shrank back when they saw who the battlers were. For the sons of Tyee were both men and gods, and when their full rage was upon them they could call upon the weapons of the gods.

So the warriors retreated to high ground to watch. The women and children withdrew still higher on the slopes, for the very air was shaking and the ground trembled as Klickitat and Wy-east snatched up great stones to hurl at each other. Loo-et was driven from the bridge. She retreated down the river to a high point, where she stood and watched, wringing her hands with grief and shame because she had been forced to forsake her fire.

Then Tyee came, riding on the wind, and his voice thundered above the thunders of the battle. . . . Too late. Klickitat and Wy-east were now high on the mountains on each side of the river, hurling still larger stones, and fire was bursting forth from the holes where the stones had been. . . .

And then the frightened people set up a great cry of terror, for the most stupendous thing of all was happening. The bridge of the gods was falling.

330

The underside crumbled first. Great fragments broke loose, turning over slowly as they fell, and the middle of the bridge began to sink down with a grinding, rumbling sound more terrible than thunder. . . . Then the whole bridge fell, smothering the river. Two high cliffs were left, facing each other, and these leaned in slowly, met, and crumbled down; and all those parts of the mountain which had supported the bridge slid down, leaving behind them wide, smoking slopes of rock which stretched all the way up to the green tops of the mountains.

The sound of it shook the earth and sky, and for a long time the echoes rolled and rumbled in the distance. The ruins of the bridge choked the river. The people dared not go down but stayed on the slope, watching the river rise up and form a long lake which glittered with reflected stars. They waited for dawn, trembling. For the first time since time began there would be no bridge in the sky, no shadow lying across the gorge. . . .

Even Klickitat and Wy-east were awed at what they had done, knowing they would be punished. Tyee came first to Wy-east; and Wy-east waited, arms folded.

"Wy-east," Tyee said sternly and sadly, "you have used the strength of the gods to quarrel over a woman, as men do."

"I have done wrong," Wy-east said. "When I saw Loo-et I forgot that I was a god."

"You know the punishment you deserve?"

"I am ready for death."

"Not death, because you are immortal. But you must stand where you are, Wy-east, until the end of time."

Then Tyee went to Klickitat, and Klickitat drew himself up, scowling. Tyee motioned him to move farther west and north. Then Tyee looked at him sadly. Fierce and untamed though Klickitat might be, he was Tyee's elder son.

"Klickitat, why did you fight Wy-east?"

"There are two of us. There is only one Loo-et."

331

"You are the elder, Klickitat. Your punishment must be greater than Wy-east's."

"A warrior dies but once."

"You may not die, my son. But because you have been so stubborn and unrepentant, you will have Loo-et near by, so that you may see her beauty each day, but you cannot speak to her or stretch out your hand to her—forever."

Then Tyee came to Loo-et, who lay on the ground, hiding her head with shame.

"This is very difficult for me, Loo-et. It was not altogether your fault. . . . And still, wasn't there a moment when you forgot your promise?"

"That is true. When Wy-east stood beside my fire I forgot I was old at heart and remembered only that I was beautiful. May I have my fire again, Tyee?"

"No. I will teach the people to build their own fires so that they will not have to depend upon borrowing coals. . . . And this is your punishment, Loo-et. You will remain where you are forever—close to Klickitat, but where you can see Wy-east across the river. Do not fear Klickitat. He cannot speak to you or lay a hand upon you. . . . That is all, Loo-et."

"Wait, Spirit-Chief! If I can see Wy-east across the river, he can also see me. . . ."

"So?" Tyee laughed. "Very well. After all, you kept your fire burning these many years. You may be beautiful, Loo-et."

"Forever?"

"Forever."

When morning came the people saw that the river was pouring through the ruins of the bridge in long, foaming cascades. They came down to the river's edge—timidly, afraid. . . . But the sunlight was bright in the canyon. Though the bridge was gone, the river was rolling on, as usual. The salmon were leaping in the swift water.

And far up in the mountains to the south they saw a great

peak standing in the forest, tall and slender and motionless, his head touching the clouds. White men later called him Mount Hood, but the people knew that it was proud and calm Wy-east.

Far to the northwest stood a more rough-hewn, truculent peak. It was Klickitat, and to the people of the river he will always be Klickitat, though white men call him Mount Adams.

And near by was the most perfect peak of all—incomparably graceful of form, clothed from head to foot in cold and dazzling white. . . . St. Helens? No. That is the name used by those who do not know the legend of the Bridge of the Gods. It is Loo-et. Beautiful Loo-et . . . who looks across the river smilingly, knowing that even the shadow of Klickitat can never touch her and she will be beautiful in the eyes of Wy-east forever.

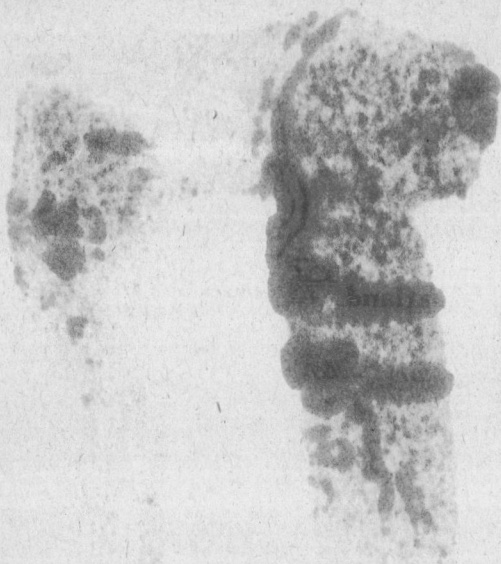

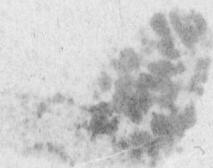

Mt. St. Helens

Mt. Adams

Astoria

Vancouver

Columbia

Mt. Hood

Portland

Oregon
City

Tualitin

Champoeg

Salem

Pacific Ocean

Willamette River

Cascade
Mountains

Umpqua

River